arrows of mercy

arrows of mercy

by philip smith

Doubleday Canada Limited, Toronto

Doubleday & Company, Inc., Garden City, New York

1969

Library of Congress Catalog Card Number 79–78662
Copyright © 1969 by Philip Smith
All Rights Reserved
Printed in the United States of America
First Edition

To Mavis, Howard, and Valerie

———————————————

author's note

In writing this story, which to the best of my belief has never before been told for the general reader, I have been helped and encouraged by many people whose kindness it is a pleasure to recall and acknowledge. My biggest debt of gratitude is to my friend Dr. W. Alexander Wielhorski, of Montreal, who not only gave me the idea from which the book eventually grew but guided me patiently through the medical intricacies that arose at every stage of its writing.

My debt to Dr. Harold R. Griffith, of Montreal, will be obvious to the reader. I am grateful to him for sharing with me the knowledge he accumulated during a fruitful lifetime in the operating room, and I hope this book will bring his outstanding achievement, already recognized within his profession of anesthesiology, to the notice of a wider public as yet, apparently, unaware of his great contribution to human welfare.

Among the many others, both inside and outside the medical profession, who responded to my requests for information in either personal interviews or correspondence, I want to thank in particular: Dr. A. E. Bennett, of Berkeley, California; Prof.

Henry K. Beecher, of Harvard Medical School and Massachusetts General Hospital; Dr. Joseph Beldavs, of Montreal; Dr. Michael S. Burman, of New York City; Dr. David A. Corey, of Knoxville, Tennessee; Prof. Stuart C. Cullen, Dean of the School of Medicine at the University of California; Mr. John J. Donohue, of New York City; Dr. Charles F. Egan, Wyandotte, Michigan; Dr. Walter Freeman, Sunnyvale, California; Mr. Norman Hartley, of Rome, Italy; Mr. B. A. Krukoff, who was for many years associated with the New York Botanical Garden and remains one of the foremost authorities on the curare plants; Dr. Heinz Lehmann, of Montreal; Mr. Michael Littlejohn, of New York City; Sir Robert Macintosh, of Oxford, England; Prof. A. R. McIntyre, of the University of Nebraska; Mrs. I. G. Mac-Leod, of Dartmouth, Nova Scotia; Dr. William B. Neff, of San Carlos, California; Dr. H. Sidney Newcomer, of Atherton, California; Dr. George T. Novinger, of Knoxville, Tennessee; Miss Violet E. Ohlsen, of Arlington, Virginia; Prof. E. M. Papper, of Columbia University and Presbyterian Hospital, New York; Dr. Frederick Prescott, of Surrey, England; Dr. K. Bryn Thomas, of Reading, England; Mr. Roger F. Varney and Dr. Oskar Wintersteiner, of the Squibb Institute for Medical Research, New Brunswick, New Jersey; Mr. Donald E. Wolf, of the Merck Sharp and Dohme Research Laboratories, Rahway, New Jersey; and Dr. Lewis H. Wright, of Great Neck, Long Island.

I am sad that three of those whose names should have been listed above have not lived to see this book in print. They are: Sir Henry Dale, O.M., one of Britain's most eminent twentieth-century scientists; Mrs. Ruth Gill, of San Rafael, California, who made me an unexpected picnic lunch and sat with me on the cliffs overlooking the Pacific recalling her life with her late husband, Richard C. Gill, in Ecuador; and Dr. John C. Burke, who initiated me into the mysteries of pharmacology at the Squibb Institute for Medical Research.

I am grateful also to three surgeons, Dr. Pierre Grondin, Dr. Eli Katz, and Dr. Breen Marien, of Montreal, who enlarged my knowledge by permitting me to watch them at work in the operating room.

My thanks are also due to the many librarians who assisted me in my research, in particular: Miss Cécile Desbarats, formerly of the Osler Library at McGill University in Montreal, as well as the staff of McGill's medical library; Mrs. Martha Benjamin, formerly of the anesthesia library at the Queen Elizabeth Hospital, Montreal; the staff of the Arthur E. Guedel Memorial Anesthesia Center in San Francisco; various information officers of the Department of Health, Education and Welfare in Washington, D.C.; and Dr. F. N. L. Poynter, director of the Wellcome Historical Medical Museum and Library, London, England.

Since much of my research was carried out in technical publications and medical papers, a bibliography would be too unwieldy for a book of this nature, as well as being inaccessible to the general reader. Two medical histories of curare have proved invaluable to me in tracking down source material and medical readers may like to know that between them they contain what is probably the most complete bibliography on the subject available. They are: *Curare, Its History and Usage,* by K. Bryn Thomas, published in England in 1963 by Pitman Medical Publishing Co. Ltd., and in North America by J. B. Lippincott Company; and *Curare, Its History, Nature and Clinical Use,* by Prof. A. R. McIntyre, University of Chicago Press, 1947.

In thanking all those who have supplied me with information, I must of course make clear that they bear no responsibility for the use I have made of it. Errors of fact or interpretation, if such there be, are mine.

Lastly, I want to thank Mr. Willis Kingsley Wing, of New York City, whose enthusiasm sustained me through a dark period in the early stages of the work; Miss Josephine Rogers, of his staff, and Mr. David Manuel, my editor at Doubleday, who have encouraged and advised me since; Mr. John G. McConnell, who generously granted me the leave of absence during which a large part of the writing was done, and Mrs. K. McCready, who typed the manuscript.

introduction

Mr. Philip Smith's book, *Arrows of Mercy*, is an absorbing account of the development of curare for use in clinical anesthesiology. Mr. Smith has the happy facility of combining extraordinary scholarship evidenced by a brilliant analysis and a complete summary of the story of the development of this most remarkable substance with a freshness of style and presentation that brings to life with bright colors the romance and the excitement of the curare story from primitive parturition to pertinent practice.

In describing how curare came to be used so widely for muscular relaxation during general anesthesia, Philip Smith has, in passing, but in considerable depth and with great fascination, summarized the history of the attempts from early times to the present to provide pain relief and unconsciousness for the performance of surgical operations. He has captured the essence of the skills of the anesthesiologist and has been able to strike that most difficult fine balance between the capable physician who administers anesthetics on the one hand with his use of anesthetic and para-anesthetic substances on the other.

In the process, Mr. Smith has also been able to place in perspective the development of all of anesthesia and the development of curare itself for muscle relaxation during surgical operations. The history of surgical skills does not escape his all-seeing eye. He has ranged from the frock coat of the pre-antiseptic era surgeon to the period of the modern transplant of hearts and other organs with consummate skill and has provided interest for both the lay and the professional reader.

Mr. Smith has brought to light some of the contributions of individuals hitherto not commonly associated with the development of the curare substances. For instance, in Chapter 5, he describes the remarkable contributions of that great genius in other scientific pursuits, Von Humboldt, in this field.

The modern era and practical development of curare for surgical anesthesia is summarized with beauty, fairness and extraordinary accuracy. The roles of Doctors Wright, Bennett, McIntyre, Newcomer, Griffith and Mr. Gill are charmingly and yet sharply portrayed.

I believe that this book will be a joy to any reader who is excited by the romance of progress in medicine, who appreciates a sparkling storyteller, and also to the professional who unfortunately sometimes loses the delicious taste of folklore and intuition in his otherwise hardheaded approach to scientific discovery.

E. M. Papper, M.D.
Professor and Chairman
Department of Anesthesiology
College of Physicians & Surgeons,
Columbia University

prologue

At the beginning of the sixteenth century, only a few years
after Columbus first saw America, an Italian friar named Peter
Martyr wrote a book describing the adventures of the earliest
Spanish explorers in that mysterious New World at the farther
end of the sea. In it, he told how an Indian "king" and seven
hundred naked warriors ambushed a party landed from a Spanish
ship to fill water barrels, "so fiercely assailing our men with their
venomous arrowes that they slew of them forty and seven . . .
for that poison is of such force that albeit the wounds were not
great, yet they died thereof immediately."

Friar Martyr thus became the first writer to refer in print to a
sinister substance so mysterious in its origin, so swift and sure in
its action, that during the centuries that followed it was to become perhaps the most feared of all poisons: curare, the "flying
death" of the Amazonian jungles.

A man struck by an arrow or blow dart tipped with curare
slumps to the ground almost immediately and dies as if be-
witched. No death struggles mark his end, and no anguished
screams. He lies, conscious but motionless, apparently resigned to

his fate, his only visible injury the wound, often insignificant, through which the poison has gained entry to his body.

Small wonder that in those credulous years, when Europe was still in the thrall of witches, curare acquired a magical reputation it was slow to lose. No legend was too strange or too terrible to be believed. The "flying death," said returning travelers, was prepared by the oldest and most decrepit women of the tribe; only when they fell dead from its fumes was it judged ready for use. To test the potency of each new batch, the Indian hunter smeared some on an arrow and fired it into a tree; if all the leaves soon fell from the tree he was assured of success in the chase. So destructive was the poison that if a man but fell asleep in the shade of the tree from which it was made, and "if one drop of the dewe of the said tree" fell into his eyes, he would be forever blind.

Years of patient scientific investigation have long since demolished these legends, but the aura of dread still clings to curare. It has been used as a murder weapon in many ingenious detective stories, movies, and television plays—and at least once in real life: in 1965, Carl Nigrisoli, a doctor in Bologna, Italy, who had been carrying on a love affair with a twenty-four-year-old girl, was found guilty of murdering his wife with an injection of a synthetic version of the drug.

The truth about curare is hardly less strange than the legends. It was prepared—and indeed is still prepared today in some remote areas—by tribal medicine men, crouched over bubbling clay pots in secret places in the jungle, boiling down the bark of several varieties of bush-ropes or lianas, according to jealously guarded formulas passed on from generation to generation. It kills in a peculiarly gruesome way: introduced into the bloodstream by even a trivial wound, it produces a progressive paralysis in which, one by one in a well-recognized sequence, the muscles of the body become utterly limp and lose their ability to perform their functions. Death comes by suffocation when the poison reaches the muscles that control breathing.

But that takes time. And all that time the victim is denied the merciful release of unconsciousness. His perceptions are undimmed—according to some reports they are even sharpened by his plight. His mind remains alert and agonizingly aware of his approaching end, but imprisoned in a helpless body. He cannot flee; he cannot raise a supplicating hand for help; he cannot even signal his panic by his expression, for his facial muscles are among the first to become paralyzed, and behind their drooping lids his eyes stare with the rigidity of the death that is soon to claim him. It is a fate beyond imagining.

On January 23, 1942, four and a half centuries after the first Spaniard fell to the "flying death," an obscure Canadian doctor named Harold Randall Griffith injected this terrible drug into the veins of a twenty-year-old plumber about to have his appendix removed in the operating room of a small hospital in Montreal. The curare did the job Harold Griffith had been confident it would, though other doctors far more eminent than he had rejected it as too dangerous ever to be tamed in the operating room. The plumber made an uneventful recovery—and the naked Indians' "venomous arrowes" had at last found their unexpected mark.

Thanks to that simple yet momentous operation, Harold Griffith is renowned within his profession today as the initiator of the greatest advance in anesthesia* since its introduction to a pain-racked world in 1846. His use of curare revolutionized the practice of anesthesia, and hence also the practice of surgery. If you are among the millions of people who have had an operation during the past quarter of a century, there is a good chance that the "flying death" may have flowed in your veins. It may well have saved your life, for in the years that have passed since that fateful operation curare has saved uncounted lives, averted untold suffering, and, more than any other single drug, made possible the marvelously intricate miracles of surgery now performed daily in the great hospitals of the world. Without curare, and the changes it has wrought in the operating room, heart transplants and many other less dramatic, though no less demanding, feats of surgery would still be as visionary as flights to the moon appeared to be only a few years ago.

---

* Oliver Wendell Holmes is generally credited with inventing the word "anaesthesia," and one wishes he had chosen a less cumbersome word. He decided that since "aesthetic" meant "sensitive," "anaesthetic" would mean "insensitive," and "anaesthesia" the condition produced. The second "a" has been dropped in American usage, though it is retained in Britain. Early practitioners of anesthesia were called anesthetists but specialists in the field today prefer to be called anesthesiologists. The term anesthetist, though still used by doctors in Britain, is reserved in the United States for a nurse trained to give anesthetics.

Science has bestowed no greater boon on humanity than anesthesia. Its introduction stilled a chorus of pain that had echoed down all the ages since some unknown caveman-surgeon, with an insight and a daring at which we in this modern world can only marvel, drove a flint into his patient's skull in the first surgical procedure of which we have definite evidence. The coming of anesthesia rescued surgery from the Dark Ages. Before 1846, the surgeon could attempt only a limited range of operations—a few inside the body, remarkably enough, but most of them confined to its surface: the opening of abscesses, the removal of superficial tumors, the amputation of arms and legs. His ability to perform even these relatively simple procedures was often restricted by the shortage of patients upon which to practice his skill, since many of the afflicted elected to face the unknown terrors of the grave rather than the only-too-well-known terrors of the operating table.

Spattered with blood, his ears assaulted by the shrieks of agony inseparable from his untender ministrations, the surgeon was compelled to work with a speed that not only courted tragic error but virtually ruled out contemplation and research. He had to await the conquest of pain before he could extend the frontiers of his knowledge. He could not know that those who would follow him would one day work calmly in the deepest privacies of the body, wielding their knives within the brain, cutting out lungs and kidneys and even, most incredible of all, the living heart.

Many other medical discoveries helped to make modern surgery possible. It could not be, for instance, had not the inspired son of an English wine merchant, Joseph Lister smeared a sticky, smelly substance called German creosote on his patients' wounds to combat the microbes he had never seen, thus banishing germs from the operating room. But anesthesia came first, and without it the surgeon could never have attained his present godlike power to confer life on millions who once would surely have died.

Yet all anesthetic agents are poisons; even the lightest dose of them can have ill effects, and an overdose can be quickly fatal. Anesthesia, for all its blessings, is thus a journey down a road that leads ultimately to death. The patient's guardian on this hazardous journey, the guide who must see that he does not take a step too far—and who must bring him back safely along the path to life after the operation—is the anesthesiologist.

Strangely, this fact is little known. No Nobel Prize has ever been awarded for achievements in anesthesia. The anesthesiologist lacks the glamor of his colleague the surgeon and the fees he commands are by no means so handsome. Patients may even resent his services, or at any rate his bill—"all he did was to ask me to count to ten, stick this needle in my arm, and now I get a bill for fifty bucks." It is a widely held conception of the anesthesiologist's role, but it is far from the truth.

Without a nod from the anesthesiologist, the surgeon will not begin to cut. Upon the anesthesiologist's knowledge and skill, and his vigilance throughout every minute of the operation, the patient's whole existence depends. If the surgical procedure demands it, the modern anesthesiologist can take his patient safely all the way along that lonely road to the brink of death. In a very real sense, he can take him over the brink—and bring him safely back again. For when the anesthesiologist has stilled the patient's lungs and taken over his breathing for him; when he has suspended the action of the patient's heart and is circulating his blood for him artificially; when he has anesthetized the patient's brain into insensibility and cut off its stream of messages to the rest of the body—when he has arrested all the vital functions that distinguish a living organism from a dead one, what mysterious spark of life remains? Is a man "dead" when a surgeon cuts out his heart and throws it away? Without the anesthesiologist to keep him alive, the answer would certainly be yes.

It is a frightening responsibility, and to discharge it with confidence the anesthesiologist, standing masked and watchful at the head of the patient, surrounded by his cylinders and tubes and pumps, needs an encyclopedic range of knowledge. Since he is the one who decides whether the patient is fit enough to survive the operation, and supervises his recovery from it, he must first be a physician. But this is only a beginning. He must also be something of a physicist, to understand the properties and the effects of the anesthetic agents in his armory. He must have some of the pharmacologist's knowledge of drugs—not only those he himself may use, but all the drugs in the family doctor's little black bag, since any one of them may react dangerously with a drug used in the operating room. He must be well versed in physiology, to understand the structure of the body and the effects upon it of his sleep-giving drugs and vapors and gases. Among his medical skills, he must be a quick and accurate diagnostician. Even if an operation lasts many hours, he must watch the patient closely and constantly for signs that something is going wrong. If anything *does* go wrong, he has little time to correct it. For instance, if the patient's pulse begins to fail and his bleeding diminishes, it may mean that not enough oxygen is reaching his brain and other vital organs. Immediately the anesthesiologist must make up his mind whether it does in fact mean this; if so, he must discover the cause of the condition and correct it. And if he takes any longer than three minutes to do all this, his patient may well die, or live out the rest of his days as a vegetable because of irreparable damage to the brain.

The modern anesthesiologist is a medical Jack-of-all-trades. But unlike Jack, he must master them all. Since he so often takes over the patient's breathing for him, he is a specialist in respiratory control. It is his responsibility to replace blood lost during the operation, so he must be something of a hematologist. To stop the patient's heart and take over the circulation of his blood, he must be a cardiovascular specialist. He should even be a passable mechanic and electrician, since so many of his duties demand the use of complicated machinery.

This is the man who now uses the "flying death" in his daily round. And out of its magic have come changes which have widened the horizons of his profession and dramatically increased his efficiency. Thanks to curare, a patient facing the surgeon's knife no longer need travel so far down that road toward death, and his chance of returning safely is immeasurably greater. This modern borrowing from the jungle sorcerer's art has also put the blessings of surgery within the feeble grasp of many who were once denied them: the old and the frail and those suffering from shock or drained of strength by their illnesses—all those unfortunates, in short, who less than a generation ago used to die because they "could not stand the anesthetic."

Three million soldiers and conscripts are said to have been pressed into the building of the Great Wall of China. Individually, dispersed as they were over fifteen hundred miles of landscape and centuries of time, they could have had little sense of joint purpose and scant realization of the eventual magnitude of their achievement. Yet each block laid by each one contributed something, no matter how small, to the whole: a monument to man's industry that has stood for two thousand years.

The bewilderingly complex structure that is modern medicine can be likened to the Great Wall, though medicine's foundation stones were laid in an even more remote era of history and some of its most important blocks remain to be fitted in place by builders not yet born. Medical history is a record of progress made slowly, step by isolated step; of significances unrealized; of discoveries made and then forgotten, so that they have had to be made again years, even centuries, later; of countless small contributions to the general fund of knowledge which, at the time they were made, often seemed as unrelated to each other as the blocks quarried for the Great Wall of China.

So it is with curare. The long struggle to pierce its cloak of superstition, to understand its seemingly magical properties and to put it to work in the service of mankind, links a legion of names, some famous, some quite unknown; some men still living, others who have been buried for centuries. Explorers, botanists, physicians, surgeons, neuropsychiatrists, physiologists, chemists, pharmacologists, veterinarians—all these and more contributed their time and talents and the fruits of their curiosity to the search.

This book attempts to tell their story. It is also the story of that great human achievement curare was destined to revolutionize—anesthesia.

part

1

chapter

1

Pain has tormented the world since long before the birth of man. Those who read prehistory from pages set in layers of rock have chipped out remains showing that dinosaurs, which vanished from the earth a hundred million years ago, suffered from arthritis, bone tumors, and even dental decay; since some dinosaurs had two thousand teeth, the agonies they must have suffered from toothache are best forgotten. And organisms similar to those that still cause disease today flourished eons before the reptiles began their 155-million-year reign of the earth: fossilized bacteria have been found in South African rock sediments dating back three billion years, halfway to the origin of this planet.

The flesh of prehistoric beings decayed long before their skeletons became fixed in the rock, so we can never be certain how many diseases, or of what type, afflicted our distant forebears. But it seems they may not have been far different from our own: the skeleton of *Pithecanthropus,* the near-human Java apeman thought to have lived more than five hundred thousand years ago, bore the signs of a diseased growth on its thigh-bone. The bones of primitive man testify that he often suffered from painful inflammation of the joints, acute enough sometimes to cause deformity—the caves in which our ancestors lived were too damp to be ideal homes.

Since early man was afflicted by disease, it is reasonable to assume that he made some attempt to treat it. Just as we can never know which prehistoric genius first learned to control fire, so the identity of the first surgeon is lost to us forever. But we do know that man's first tool, the sharpened flint, was also his first scalpel. Numerous Stone Age remains have been discovered bearing the signs of an operation known as trepanning: the cutting of a hole in the skull. It may seem incredible that such a dangerous procedure could be carried out with sharpened stones and without any form of anesthetic, but in many of the skulls new bone tissue has been formed around the cut edges, proving that the patient lived for some time after the surgery. Some skulls even bear the signs of repeated trepanning.

Primitive man blamed evil spirits for illness and the idea of this operation may have been to free the spirits from their imprisonment within the skull; it may thus have been the first treatment ever attempted for insanity, epilepsy, or blindness. But some medical historians believe trepanning might have been performed for more rational reasons. Our ancestors were no less disposed to aggression than are we, and the first medical men must have had their share of casualties with head injuries inflicted by blunt instruments. Bleeding within the skull, by building up pressure on the brain, can lead to loss of consciousness. Early man may have found by trial and error that opening the skull relieved this pressure and brought the patient back from his apparent death—a procedure still necessary today in some cases of accidental injury to the head.

Trepanning is an operation one would prefer to entrust to a modern brain surgeon. If those shaggy, beetle-browed surgical virtuosos of the Stone Age could bring it off in a badly lit cave or a clearing among the trees, with the bare ground for their operating table, it seems probable that they had mastered other forms of surgical treatment. The evidence for this is less conclusive than the trepanned skulls, but Neolithic bones have been found with healed fractures, suggesting that our ancestors realized the importance of stretching a broken limb to restore the bone to its position and then using splints to immobilize it until it healed.

4

The rest is speculation. But perhaps wounds were covered with leaves to keep out evil spirits. Gradually, through the ages, some leaves might have been found to have a more beneficent effect than others—and the foundations of plant medicine would have been laid. Doctors, deprived of the evidence of early medical practice by the passage of time, have turned to the study of primitive tribes still living in an attempt to hold up a mirror to the past.

Australian aborigines, to whom plaster of Paris was as foreign as penicillin, were found to be encasing broken arms and legs in soft clay, which hardened into a serviceable cast when it dried. In America, some Indian tribes used a similar treatment, binding up fractures with wet rawhide which also immobilized the limb as it dried. The Indians, too, used to pack wounds with hot sand and bind them with leaf poultices, and since they kept wounds clean, and isolated their injured from the rest of the tribe, they often achieved better results than their Western counterparts, who less than a century ago still ridiculed the idea that cleanliness was vital to surgery.

Stone Age man may also have known how to stitch wounds, since bone needles have been found in his caves. Or perhaps he used thorns to pin together torn flesh, as some African tribes still do. Another primitive method of suturing wounds seen in various parts of the world is to bring the cut edges of the flesh together and permit ants with pincer-like jaws to bite through them. When the ants' bodies are severed, the jaws remain in place, serving precisely the same function as the metal clips used in modern surgery. When we pass from prehistory to the earliest recorded civilizations, we find surgery already well established. Circumcision is known to have been practiced six thousand years ago, though since it was performed for religious or ritual reasons it was perhaps not true surgery. However, the famous Code drawn up by the Babylonian lawmaker Hammurabi twenty-two centuries before Christ laid down a scale of fees for surgeons. It said:

"If a physician make a severe wound on a man with a bronze lancet and save the man's life; or if he open an abscess in a man's eye with a bronze lancet and save that man's eye, he shall receive ten shekels of silver.

"If it be a man's slave, the owner of the slave shall give two shekels of silver to the physician."

Fees graduated to the social or economic status of the patient thus had an ancient beginning. The punishment prescribed by Hammurabi for surgeons who made a mistake or had the bad luck to lose a patient was rather more strict than the most punitive modern malpractice suit: "If a physician shall make a severe wound with an operating knife and kill him, or shall open an abscess with an operating knife and destroy the eye, his hands shall be cut off."

The first textbook of surgery known to us—though apparently not the first one written since it seems to be based in part on still more ancient works—dates from about 1600 B.C. The portion of it that survives is inscribed on a papyrus roll about fifteen feet long discovered by the American Egyptologist Edwin Smith at Luxor a century ago but deciphered only many years later. It describes forty-eight cases of fractures, dislocations, wounds, and tumors and prescribes techniques for treating them, one or two of which have changed little in the intervening centuries. In several cases, the author, who apparently had had some experience as a battlefield surgeon, recommended the application of fresh meat to wounds; the beefsteak treatment for a black eye thus goes back much further than Grandmother's day. Thanks no doubt to the practice of mummifying bodies, the ancient Egyptians also knew and described most forms of bandages used in modern hospitals.

Another papyrus from around the same period as Edwin Smith's, in addition to detailing ten types of beer in which medicines might conveniently be taken, describes methods of removing wrinkles and moles, and other forms of cosmetic treatment. Plastic surgery is considered a fairly recent innovation, yet five or six centuries before Christ there was a flourishing school of surgery devoted to it in India. Adulterers in those days were punished by having their noses cut off, and since demand for any commodity quite often produces a supply of it, a caste of potters grew up whose specialty was to rebuild noses. Extraordinarily enough, they were able to perfect an operation called rhinoplasty which is still considered a difficult one—it was rediscovered in Europe by an English surgeon named Joseph Carpue at the beginning of the nineteenth century. The technique was to cut flaps of skin from the cheek or forehead and use them—still connected to the place from which they were taken, so that the tissue would

6

not die—to mold a new nose. Hollow reeds were inserted into the built-up flesh to keep the nostrils open.

A celebrated Indian surgeon, Sushruta, used gourds and watermelons to teach students how to make various intricate incisions and described one hundred and twenty-five different surgical instruments. Hindu surgeons reputedly had steel knives sharp enough to split a hair. They knew how to remove a patient's tonsils, which is by no means the "minor" operation it is usually considered, and there is evidence that they were able to perform successful Caesarean operations, removing a baby from the mother's womb with such skill that both mother and child survived. This operation was not done successfully in Europe until the sixteenth or seventeenth century—medical authorities disagree about the date.

Incredibly, all these operations were carried out without anesthetics as we know them, though early Hindu manuals mention that patients undergoing operations inhaled the fumes of burning hemp, known in the east as hashish or bhang—and to westerners as marijuana. "Pot" has lately enjoyed a surprising revival in the west, but the most nihilistic hippie would probably prefer ether as an anesthetic. If hemp could be considered an anesthetic at all, it must certainly have been a crude one and its benefits to the patient must have been at best uncertain.

Another early reference to anesthesia occurs in a Chinese work of about 300 B.C.—though the accuracy of the report seems as open to question as the nature of the surgical procedure the anesthesia was allegedly designed to facilitate. It appears that a surgeon named Pien Ch'iao gave two men a "toxic drink" that rendered them unconscious for three days, which is somewhat longer than the most expert anesthesiologist would care to keep his patient insensible nowadays. The intrepid Pien Ch'iao then performed a gastrostomy on one of the men. This is an operation sometimes carried out when a patient is unable to eat; it consists of opening a hole into the stomach through the abdominal wall. Pien Ch'iao went on to "explore the heart." After which, with an ingenuity unrivaled in his profession until the advent of Dr. Christiaan Barnard twenty-three centuries later, he "removed and interchanged their hearts," gave the men a "wonderful drug" and sent them home fully restored, and no doubt marveling at his skill.

7

Though we may doubt the authenticity of this surgical tour-de-force, one operation certainly performed in China a thousand years before Christ was castration, to provide a supply of eunuchs for the Imperial Courts. The testicles of the unfortunates chosen for this dubious honor were sliced off with a semicircular knife and preserved in alcohol for the rest of their owner's life—since a Chinese who had become separated from any of the normal quota of limbs and organs was unable to join his ancestors in the better world after death. An anesthetic of undisclosed composition is supposed to have been used for this operation, but it is unlikely that it was any more effective than the quick punch on the jaw said by visitors to the Imperial Court to have been administered to men still being subjected to this same operation in the nineteenth century.

Hua To, who was born a century or so after Christ, lived to the wise old age of ninety and became so famous in China that he was worshipped as the god of surgery. He is said to have made his patients drink wine in which an effervescent powder had been dissolved and then, for some unfathomable reason, to have opened their abdomens and washed the contents while they were still numb from the effects of the drink. If Hua To did in fact possess the secret of anesthesia, so long before anyone else, it is difficult not to admire the forbearance of a general who was treated by him for an arrow wound in the arm; instead of giving him the benefit of this bubbly anesthetic, the old surgeon had him watch a game of chess to divert his attention from the operation.

The ancient Chinese were not the only people to make deities out of their surgeons. A Thessalonian chief named Asklepios, who fought in the Trojan wars, devised an instrument for extracting arrowheads from wounds and performed other feats of surgical virtuosity that won him the admiration of his fellow Greeks. Myths soon obscured Asklepios's real achievements. According to one legend, he cured a girl swollen by dropsy by cutting off her head and hoisting her up by the heels to allow the accumulated fluids to run out of her body—completing this highly original procedure by stitching the head back on.

Clearly, Asklepios was divinely inspired, but such interference with the foreordained laws of life and death could not go unnoticed. Pluto eventually complained that Asklepios's earthly ministrations were depleting the supply of souls for Hell, and

8

Zeus obligingly sent a thunderbolt to destroy him. Within a few centuries, Asklepios was venerated as a god and temples manned by a caste of priest-surgeons were erected in his honor. The Romans knew him as Aesculapius and his symbol—a pair of snakes entwined around a staff—is today's most widely recognized medical emblem.

Fortunately for the future welfare of humanity, the priestly disciples of Aesculapius gradually devoted more and more time to their religious duties and, preoccupied with the souls of their patients, passed their ailing bodies over to lay assistants. Trained in the taut Greek disciplines of philosophy and logic, these laymen soon began to question the supernatural tenets of the Asklepian cult—after all, replacing severed heads is a testing assignment for a surgeon armed only with faith. Patient observation of the symptoms of disease and accurate recording of the results of its treatment replaced superstition as the basis of Greek medical practice.

The greatest of the Greek medical schools was on the island of Cos, where a ruined temple of Aesculapius still stands. There, five centuries before Christ, one of the Asklepian lay doctors had a son, whom he christened Hippocrates. After studying in Athens, Hippocrates traveled throughout Greece as an itinerant physician and, by closely studying each patient instead of attributing his illness to the gods, founded the science of medicine.

Some of the case histories so carefully kept by Hippocrates have come down to us and they are considered by modern doctors to be model records. The Greek surgeons introduced few operations that had not been tried by their predecessors in earlier times, though they did refine some techniques. Their supreme achievement was to provide a rational basis for medicine—even though their scientific methods were destined to be forgotten for many centuries after their time, and not introduced to Europe until the Renaissance.

Hippocrates and the Greeks studied the effect of disease and injury on the human body and introduced more thorough methods of diagnosis; they set down a literature of surgery so that practitioners could measure their successes against, and compare their experiences with, those of their fellows. A description by Hippocrates of a woman with "quinsy" is clearly recognizable by modern doctors as a case of diphtheria; and unlike many other doctors, before and since, Hippocrates did not shrink from recording that his patient died. He need not have been ashamed: diphtheria was not finally defeated until this century.

Some treatments prescribed by Hippocrates for dislocations are not much different from modern forms of treatment—except that he had to carry them out without anesthetics. Such was the great doctor's humanity—his code of ethics still governs the conduct of doctors around the world—that had effective anesthetics been available he would certainly have taken advantage of them.

The Greeks did in fact have a word for anesthesia: they called it *nodynia,* meaning *ease from pain.* But as for their means of attaining this desirable state, it is difficult to tell where fable ended and fact began. Who would blame the careful Hippocrates for not placing too much faith in lettuce as an anesthetic? But Pliny advised pounding it with vinegar and taking it twice a month to banish toothache, and after the death of Adonis, Venus threw herself down on a bed of lettuce "to lull her grief and repress her desires."

Another plant thought to relieve pain was dittany, and Venus, who appears to have been a great believer in plant lore, administered it to her son Aeneas after he had been wounded in battle. Dittany grew on the island of Crete where, according to Aristotle, wild goats wounded by arrows sought it out since it was "supposed to have the property of ejecting arrows from the body." Whether because there was a germ of truth in some of these old legends, or merely because legends die hard, a Welsh book published many centuries later recommended dittany as an antidote to pain, and it was used in parts of rural England as a remedy for toothache until quite recently.

Of even more dubious value was another Greek painkiller, a form of marble known as Memphis stone, which was supposed to be crushed and mixed with vinegar; when spread on the skin this was claimed to produce numbness. Again, there is no record of Hippocrates using it, but it was still being touted as late as the sixteenth century—though by this time the recommendation was that it be drunk, not merely smeared on the skin.

Some of the plants used by the Greeks and other ancients in their unsuccessful attempts to overcome pain undoubtedly had narcotic properties, meaning that they could bring on sleep and lessen sensation. Our word "narcotic" comes from the Greek *narkē,* meaning "stupor." The most widely used of these plants, and the one about which the wildest legends grew up, was the mandrake, or mandragora. This plant—not the "May apple" or mandrake of America—had a thick, forked root shaped rather like a man's body. All sorts of supernatural qualities were attributed to it, not the least of them being that it was a powerful aphrodisiac.

The Greeks believed an evil spirit lodged in the root of the mandrake and that when the plant was pulled from the ground it emitted an unearthly shriek. No one has ever recorded hearing this shriek—because to hear it was to die on the spot. The harvesting of such a lethal crop presented an unusual problem. But this was neatly solved by tying a dog to the plant, retiring to a safe distance, calling the dog, and then blowing a piercing blast on a horn to protect your ears from the fearful wail as the struggling dog tore the mandrake from the earth.

You lost a lot of dogs this way, but you were rewarded with possession of a plant which, when dissolved in wine or some other liquid, or baked into a cake, would produce a sleep lasting three or four hours, during which you would be insensible to all earthly cares. "Physicians use it when they have to resort to cutting or burning," wrote Pliny the Elder. His nephew, Pliny the Younger, was even more convinced of the efficiency of the mandrake. "It is sufficient for some persons to seek sleep from the smell," he wrote. The mandrake was still being prescribed as late as 1660, as one ingredient of a "sleeping apple" alleged to produce insensibility when smelled.

Two other plants mentioned in the earliest medical texts have a more respectable history as pain-relievers, and indeed are still used in modern medicine. They are henbane, which, like mandragora, is a member of the deadly nightshade family, and the much more widely known opium. As the name indicates, henbane, a mild narcotic, was judged poisonous to chickens. But its alternative name, *hyoscyamus* (swine-bean), suggests that it was good for pigs. Dioscorides, a famous Greek physician of the first century A.D. who served in Nero's army, wrote that the juice of the plant and its dried seeds were "prepared for lotions to take away pain."

In the early years of this century, henbane's modern counterpart, scopolamine (known in England as hyoscine), was com-

11

bined with morphine, which comes from opium, to produce "twilight sleep," a form of anesthesia which had a considerable vogue in childbirth until it was gradually decided that it did not so much take away the pains of labor as make the mother forget them afterwards.

Opium, the dried milky juice of the little bulb just below the petals of the poppy, was used as a drug long before Dioscorides described it as a "pain-easer and a sleep-causer." In ancient Egypt, it was used by the first woman doctor of whose existence we are aware, the goddess Tefnut; with its aid, she cured a headache that had been bothering the Great God Ra. The ancients administered opium in wine, but while it is a powerful narcotic it could not have been given in doses large enough to approach true anesthesia without dangerously interfering with the patient's breathing.

That was the trouble with all attempts to use narcotics as a form of anesthesia. An anesthetic must not only put the patient to sleep but must keep him asleep—and motionless—throughout whatever cuts and manipulations the surgeon finds necessary. True anesthesia produces an insensitivity to pain so profound that it is equaled only in death. Narcotics have the power to dull pain in varying degrees. But if given in doses large enough to produce complete and continuing insensitivity to pain they are only too likely not merely to imitate death but to cause it.

The Greeks, in common with both earlier and later practitioners of the healing arts, used another substance in their attempt to numb the patient about to submit to the surgeon's knife: alcohol, sometimes spiked with one or more of the other supposed pain-killers, sometimes neat. Since surgery before the introduction of anesthesia was often scarcely distinguishable from execution, it is perhaps no accident that condemned men were also given the same medicine. "If a man is led forth to death," said the Talmud a few centuries after Christ, "he is given a cup of spiced wine to drink, whereby his soul is wrapped in night."

Night blots out many things, but it was no more able than narcotics to blot out the pain of surgery. Nevertheless, alcohol —often laced with laudanum, or tincture of opium—was probably as good an anesthetic as any available until the introduction of ether in 1846. Even since then, many a soldier on the battlefield or traveler in far places has endured an emergency operation with no more than a slug of whisky to brace him for the ordeal. And if the surgeon, oppressed in those dark days before anesthesia by the agony his knife was about to inflict, sometimes took a fortifying tot himself, who is to blame him?

chapter

2

After the Greeks came the Romans. Superior technology, as it sometimes does still, conquered reason. Skill in plumbing and building fine straight roads came to be valued more highly than the intellectual triumphs of the Greeks, almost as though victor were jealous of vanquished and fearful of his ideas. The Romans, whose weekends were not complete unless they could watch human blood spilt in the arena, who took men's lives in sport, recoiled in hypocritical horror at the prospect of invading the privacy of the human corpse to seek knowledge that might aid the living.

Galen, the last of the great Greek doctors, was compelled to teach anatomy without the aid of a demonstration skeleton, and his belief that a woman had two wombs—one for boys and one for girls—indicates how crippling this prohibition on dissection proved to be. It was tragic too, for future generations, since Galen's teachings were to be held sacrosanct for the next fifteen centuries. Gradually the medical knowledge so painfully acquired by earlier civilizations was lost—or at best mislaid. When Rome fell, medicine entered upon more than a thousand years of darkness.

The early Christian church retained the prohibition on dissection, for was not man made in the image of God? To defile the human body was the worst kind of impiety—except, perhaps, on the rack or at the stake. The practice of medicine passed into the hands of monks, and at a time when monasteries cheerfully bought milk claimed to have sprung from the breasts of the Virgin, only Heaven could help the sick. As rational medicine was eclipsed, the saints came marching in.

Saint Augustine, in the fifth century A.D., declared that "All diseases of Christians are to be ascribed to demons." And for a cure, what better idea than to pray to the saints? Saint Agatha had had her breasts cut off, so she became the patron saint of women with breast complaints. For toothache, you turned to Saint Appollonia, for had not her teeth been pulled out at her martyrdom? Saint Lawrence watched over—it would be too much to say protected—those with back ailments, and Saint Just those with headaches. Echoes of those benighted days are still heard today: chorea—a nerve disease which experimenters were to try much later to cure with the mysterious curare—is still known as St. Vitus's dance.

The humane precepts of Hippocrates, the sage advice he based on sane observation, were discarded. Amulets and incantations formed the physician's stock-in-trade. Fever was treated with a splinter from a doorway through which a eunuch had passed; an early Anglo-Saxon medical manual recommended that the "medicine" for a man possessed by the devil—a strange mixture of herbs, ale, and holy water over which seven masses had been sung—should be drunk out of church bells for best results. An epileptic, it was said, might benefit from having pieces of roasted cuckoo blown up his nostrils.

That such insanities should have held men's minds not merely for generations but for centuries defies understanding. The Royal Society was first incorporated in London in 1662 to band together learned men in the study of science, to propagate and take advantage of the great discoveries already beginning to be made. Yet one of its first tasks was to investigate the efficacy of unicorn horn as an antidote for poison. Unicorn horn, in that it did not even exist, was a vastly more wholesome medicine than

15

most of the others prescribed by doctors of the day. To mention just a few among the grisly collection, there were wood lice, the bowels of moles cut open alive, bats' blood, the oil and flesh of vipers, bile, foxes' lungs, spiders' webs, saliva from a fasting man and sweat from a fat one, human placenta, the urine of a lizard and the dung of virtually every animal known to man—and some, like the unicorn, that weren't.

The physicians who prescribed these revolting remedies considered themselves more than a cut above surgeons. In the twelfth and thirteenth centuries, a series of ecclesiastical decrees had stipulated that the shedding of blood was incompatible with the functions of the priesthood and abhorrent to the church generally—the Crusades didn't count, apparently. So inflexible was the principle of divine predestination considered that some monks were forbidden to see a doctor or take medicine when ill; in the light of the depths to which the medical arts had sunk, this was perhaps not so great a deprivation as it sounds.

The effect of these decrees was to relegate the practice of surgery to barbers and such lesser souls as executioners, brothel-keepers, and those lowly practitioners who wandered the countryside castrating and spaying farm animals. As late as Frederick the Great's day, Prussian army surgeons numbered among their duties the shaving of officers.

Surgery was thus confined for many years largely to the repair of wounds, the cutting away of skin tumors, the setting of broken bones and the replacement of dislocated ones. Amputations were avoided wherever possible because of the danger of infection and the difficulty of controlling the inevitable bleeding: the ligatures used by the Greeks to tie off blood vessels had gone the way of the rest of their knowledge and the usual treatment for hemorrhage was to cauterize the stump with red-hot irons or plunge it into boiling oil.

One class of itinerant specialists essayed to cut into the bladders of conscious patients to remove those painful deposits known as stones, an operation termed lithotomy. The method they used was exactly the same as that used by Hindu surgeons centuries before: the patient was laid on his back with his knees drawn up on his chest and held by a couple of strong men; the operator placed a finger into the rectum, located the stone and hooked it down so that it made a bump on the tight skin between the buttocks; he then cut through the skin into the bladder and pulled out the stone. Having collected his fee, he moved on, without waiting to see whether his patient recovered.

The technique by which Samuel Pepys was "cut for the stone" in 1658 was probably not much of an improvement on this, though it was carried out by an expert lithotomist of the day, Thomas Hollyer, surgeon to St. Thomas's Hospital. It would have been fascinating to have Pepys' account of the operation, but it occurred before he began to keep his famous diary. It was the custom then to be operated on at the home of a friend or relative and Pepys chose the house of his niece, Mrs. Turner, in Salisbury Court. His feet were tied to his hands and a porter stood on each side of the table holding his legs. The head porter sat on his chest, partly to hold him still and partly, no doubt, to shield his eyes from what was going on.

The operation was a success, except that the diarist's sperm ducts were severed—a common hazard of this operation for centuries. Though the diaries show that this did not impair his sexual appetite, it made him sterile.

The pain of such an ordeal can be imagined, but the pain of the stone evidently made it worth while. Every year, on the anniversary of the operation, Pepys and some of his friends, with Dr. Hollyer, would gather at Mrs. Turner's house for a thanksgiving dinner of carp and salmon, roast chicken, tongue, cheese, and good strong drink—which undoubtedly was the only anesthetic available to him for the operation.

If surgery advanced little for centuries after the ancients, attempts to relieve its attendant agonies progressed not at all. In 1591 a Scottish woman named Eufame Macalyne was burned at the stake, for daring to seek relief from the pangs of childbirth—"In sorrow," it had been written in Genesis, "thou shalt bring forth children." In seventeenth-century France, Nicolas Bailly, a barber-surgeon who gave a narcotic to a patient before an operation, was fined for practicing witchcraft. And attempts to produce anesthesia by the giving of herbal potions were subsequently declared illegal throughout France.

Not that many attempts were made. The most widely used of all supposed "anesthetics" during the Middle Ages was the "sleeping sponge," an ordinary bathroom sponge soaked in the juices of a variety of plants which, when held to the patient's

17

nostrils, was reputed to produce unconsciousness. The concoctions with which the sponge should be saturated varied according to the medical authority prescribing them, but they included most, if not all, of the "sleep-giving" plants known to the Greeks. Mandragora, whose shrieks dispatched so many dogs, was almost universal. One of the simplest recipes advanced used only three ingredients: opium, mandragora, and henbane root. Others added to these basics enough plants to fill several pages in a botanical encyclopedia, including the unripe mulberry, hemlock, wood-ivy, forest mulberry, seeds of lettuce, dock and sorrel.

In the unlikely event that this mixture produced the desired unconsciousness, the patient could be brought round—assuming that the first cut of the knife did not do it only too effectively—by proffering him another sponge soaked in vinegar. Many years ago, an American anesthesiologist, perhaps inspired by earnestness but more probably by whimsicality, mixed up this medieval witches' brew, soaked a sponge in it, and tried it out on several animals. It did not, he reported, make even a guinea pig nod.

One early writer, advancing a prescription for a sleeping sponge, also advised any surgeon planning to use it to truss up his patient securely—as good an indication of the method's effectiveness as any. His lack of faith was evidently shared by many medieval practitioners, since use of the sleeping sponge was introduced, abandoned, and then introduced again throughout the Middle Ages. The problem, as always until 1846, was that there was no alternative—unless we count a thirteenth-century formula alleged to produce a sleep lasting four days. This began: "Get a penny-weight of the wax from a dog's ear . . ."

Medieval medical literature makes dreary reading. Physicians as well as surgeons were shackled by their almost complete lack of understanding of how the body worked in health, let alone in sickness. Long after the Renaissance had begun to free men's minds from ignorance and superstition, doctors believed four "humors" governed the balance of the human body, and that these humors were governed in turn by the four natural elements of air, earth, water, and fire. The stomach was an oven fed by heat from the liver, the heart a perpetual fountain of blood.

On the battlefield, traditional training ground of the surgeon, tinkers and other tradesmen smeared wounds with ointments compounded from grease used on the hoofs of horses, cobblers' wax, and rust from old kettles. Ugly rivers of pus streamed from every wound and were considered essential to healing as late as the nineteenth century, when the dangers of infection began to be recognized.

The art of medicine, such as it was, lacked the solid underpinning of science. And strangely, it was artists who took the first unwitting steps along the road medicine had to follow. From the fourteenth century on, the great cultural and intellectual currents radiating from Italy began to release Europe from the stagnation of medievalism. Their curiosity fired by the new freedom of thought, Renaissance artists like Michelangelo and Leonardo da Vinci began to seek their inspiration in reality and to study not only the form but the structure and function of the human body. In their quest for knowledge, they even assisted at dissections performed by surgeons. Leonardo set out to study bones and muscles for art's sake but went on to make important contributions to the knowledge of internal organs. Had his drawings been more widely disseminated in his own day, he might today be considered the father of modern anatomy.

Instead that honor goes to Andreas Vesalius, who was born into a family of doctors in Brussels in 1514. Stocky and strong in both body and will, the young Vesalius had far more than the normal boy's interest in animals; he wanted to know what went on beneath their skins. Whenever he caught a frog or a mouse he would slowly and meticulously cut it up to examine its structure. By the time he began his formal medical studies he had taught himself a great deal about anatomy. He had also acquired so much skill at dissection that soon he was impatiently pushing aside his instructors and cutting up cadavers himself.

Professors of surgery in those days, despite the occasional evidence of their own eyes, were still teaching anatomy as it had been taught by Galen, who derived his knowledge from studying animals. Assuming that man shared the structures of the animals, Galen said human hipbones were flared as in the ox. When Vesalius proved him to be mistaken by careful observation of skeletons he himself cut down from the gallows—at the risk of execution had he been discovered—the credulous sixteenth-century medical establishment decided not that the venerated Galen was wrong, but that the shape of man's hipbones had become distorted by his adoption of trousers instead of togas.

Vesalius's great teachings on anatomy, though only slowly learned by the medical profession, are recognized today as the first indispensable foundation stone in the building of modern surgery. The next was laid by an Englishman who lived during the reign of the first Queen Elizabeth and was ten years old in 1588, when his countrymen defeated the Armada and broke the power of Spain. William Harvey was the first of seven sons born to a prosperous Kentish merchant and he seems to have decided to become a doctor long before he entered Cambridge.

Notwithstanding the first big blow struck at Galen's theories by Vesalius, the world in Harvey's day still accepted the old Greek's explanation of the function of the heart. Had it been in any way true, this would have been a masterpiece of theoretical deduction. The liver, said Galen, converted the food we eat into "natural spirits." The blood ebbed and flowed through the body like a sort of red tide, picking up these natural spirits like seaweed along the way. Part of this fortified blood passed via the right side of the heart into the lungs, where it was "purified." The rest passed from the right side of the heart into the left—infiltrating through invisible pores in the septum, which divides the heart into its four chambers—and the left side of the heart converted the liver's natural spirits into the equally mysterious "vital spirits." Some of these vital spirits animated the other organs, such as the kidneys and intestines, and the rest were carried into the brain, where they generated "animal spirits," which coursed through the nerves and gave us the power of movement and the senses of touch and smell.

Harvey suspected this was nonsense, and proved it later in what is probably the most important single medical work ever printed: a small, seventy-two-page book entitled *Exercitatio Anatomica De Motu Cordis et Sanguinis in Animalibus*. Galen's neat theory, if not actually Holy Writ, was considered so by the medical profession. And for a doctor to challenge it must have seemed not merely heretical but evidence of doubtful sanity—as if today an astronomer were to spend years peering through the Mount Palomar telescope and then announce, gravely, that the earth is flat.

Only twenty-five years before Harvey was born, the Spaniard Michael Servetus wrote that the blood passed from one side of the heart to the other through the lungs, which in fact it does.

20

For this, and other heresies incautiously voiced in the same book, he was burned at the stake. Harvey was probably never in danger of being roasted alive, though he was once arraigned on a flimsy charge of poisoning King James I, to whom he was Physician Extraordinary. Nevertheless, he made sure that his explanation of the circulation of the blood was impregnable before he gave it to the world.

Leonardo da Vinci, as Harvey may or may not have known, recognized that at the bases of the two great arteries conducting blood away from the heart, the aorta and the pulmonary artery, there were valves which prevented the flow from reversing and returning into the heart. And Fabricius, Harvey's friend and teacher in the great medical school at Padua, had demonstrated that valves in the veins of the arms and legs directed the flow of blood toward the heart, though Fabricius himself took this as confirmation of Galen's "ebb-and-flow" teaching. When he returned from Padua and took a post at St. Bartholomew's Hospital in London, Harvey spent fourteen years pondering the problem, looking for incontrovertible evidence and resisting the temptation to erect theories until he found it. He dissected more than eighty different types of animals and found that all the valves in all their veins always pointed in such a way that the blood could only flow though them *toward* the heart. In the arteries there were no valves at all, apart from those described by da Vinci, so that arterial blood could only flow *away* from the heart.

He satisfied himself there were no pores, invisible or otherwise, in the septum dividing the two sides of the heart. Painstakingly he measured the quantity of blood in the body, how much could be held in the blood vessels, how much in the chambers of the heart. If Galen's theory were correct, he decided, the heart would pump out in ten minutes two or three times as much blood as all the body's arteries and veins could hold.

In 1628, he was ready. He published his book in Frankfurt, then the center of the publishing trade, announcing his revolutionary discovery to a world in which, it has been said, not one man over forty believed it during Harvey's lifetime. The heart, said Harvey, is a muscle; the blood is pumped from its left side and carried around the body by the arteries; it returns to the heart through the veins and is then pumped out again by the

21

right side on a shorter journey, through the lungs and back to the left side of the heart, where the whole cycle begins over again.

Many mysteries remained hidden from Harvey. He did not know the lungs supplied the blood with oxygen, for the discovery of oxygen was still more than a century away. Nor did he know how the blood passed from the arteries to the veins, for the discovery of the tiny capillaries that link them had to await the invention of the microscope. But his system of experiment, observation, and measurement put medical research back on the rails of reason and ended its domination by mysticism and theology. No more "animal" spirits frolicking through our bodies? The heart a mere muscle, and not the seat of love? It was a revolutionary concept—and one to which we have not yet entirely adjusted, at least in our romantic imagery.

Years had to pass before Harvey's work was digested and developed and put to practical use in the evolving science of surgery. But one of his contemporaries who was much impressed was the versatile Sir Christopher Wren, who conceived the notion of injecting drugs directly into an animal's bloodstream—and thus foreshadowed intravenous anesthesia, which in today's hospitals makes "going under" so much less terrifying than it used to be. In 1656, Wren persuaded his friend the chemist Robert Boyle to cooperate with him in an experiment carried out on a dog at Oxford. They attached a quill to a syringe, stuck it into a vein in the dog's leg and injected a solution of opium. The dog lost consciousness but survived. In a later experiment, it died. Wren was many years ahead of his time—if not as a designer of cathedrals at least as an anesthesiologist. For Harvey had been dead almost two centuries before pain was banished from the operating room.

During those two centuries, surgeons used the lessons Vesalius and Harvey had taught them to devise operations so drastic that it is difficult to imagine their being performed without anesthetics. Early in 1819 a Dutch doctor named C. B. Tilanus watched the greatest French surgeon of his day, Guillaume Dupuytren, display his mastery of technique by removing a tumor from the lower jaw of a thirty-nine-year-old man. "One incision divides the underlip and extends to the tongue bone," wrote Tilanus later. "A second one from the far side of the affected skin joins the first incision under the chin. The flap of skin is removed,

22

the jaw exposed and from both sides of the gap a piece taken either by sawing until it reaches the sound bone, or broken off with bone snippers so that the distance between the two sides is now two and a half inches . . . The soft portions of the jaw are also removed where unsound, and blood vessels tied at the same time."

The operation, Tilanus commented, was a difficult one and "took a considerable time." And all that time, while those great gashes were being cut in his face and pieces of his jaw were being broken off, the patient was fully conscious. He died, as may be imagined, but not until thirteen days after the operation.

The agonies endured on the operating table before the introduction of anesthesia can be compared only to those of the torture chamber. Men—and women—killed themselves rather than face the horrors of surgery. Some went out of their minds. On the table, an occasional stoic submitted bravely to the knife, only gritted teeth and involuntary flinchings of his muscles betraying his suffering. Most surgical patients, though, writhed desperately against the straps that bound them and screamed incessantly, cursing or praying to God, pleading with the surgeon to stop and when that failed frantically imploring him to hurry.

Often, the ordeal was more than they could bear. Some died of what was euphemistically termed "exhaustion of the nervous powers"; in fact, they had been tortured to death, as surely as if they had been in the hands of the Inquisition. As Dupuytren once said: "Pain kills like hemorrhage."

The patient's only ally against the agony of these operations was the swiftness with which the surgeon could accomplish them: torture inflicted for one minute was obviously better than torture inflicted for two minutes—or for twenty. For a while, surgeons were rated, like racehorses, by their speed.

One of the undoubted champions was Robert Liston, a tall, heavily built Scot who reveled in his strength and boasted that he did not need tourniquets: amputating a leg with a few quick flashes of his knife and a couple of strokes of his saw, Liston would halt the spurt of blood by tightly grasping the thigh with his massive left hand. He often took on patients none of his fellow surgeons would tackle. One of these was a sixteen-year-old boy with a massive aneurysm, or swelling, of an artery running beneath his shoulder blade. Liston opened a foot-long incision

23

in the boy's back through which to work but as soon as he cut into the swelling a torrent of blood gushed out and the boy collapsed. Imperturbably Liston pulled open the rest of the aneurysm and thrust his left index finger into the artery to plug it. Then, still stemming the flood with his left hand, he cut away a large portion of the diseased shoulder blade with his right. The boy recovered from the operation but died several months later from a recurrence of the disease.

The great surgeons were not indifferent to the suffering they caused their patients. William Cheselden, so skillful that he could cut out a bladder stone in fifty-four seconds, was unable to sleep on the night before an important operation. John Abernethy, another famous English surgeon, affected a bluff, intimidating manner with his patients, in the belief that this would inspire their confidence—but after an operation he would rush out of the operating room and vomit. As a medical student, Sir James Young Simpson, later to play an important role in the popularization of anesthesia, watched a woman having her breast amputated then fled in horror to Parliament House, Edinburgh, to seek work as a clerk. He returned to his studies later, but asked: "Can nothing be done to make operations less painful?"

The answer, as it had been throughout history, was still "No." As science began to dislodge the supernatural from its sovereignty over medicine and faith in the pain-killing properties of lettuce and screaming roots withered away, some surgeons experimented with other methods of relieving the torments of surgery. They were scarcely more successful than the ancients. One method revived from time to time was a technique practiced by the Assyrians—the application of pressure to the carotid arteries, the two big arteries in the neck which carry blood to the brain. Cutting off the supply of blood to the brain certainly produces unconsciousness, but if prolonged it is also fatal, so that what purported to be a method of easing pain really amounted to throttling the patient half to death.

A variation of this technique also tried was to apply the pressure not to arteries but to nerves, the idea being that compressing the main nerve of the thigh or upper arm would eliminate the pain of an operation lower down the limb. Fearsome-looking iron clamps covered with leather were fashioned for this purpose but they had several disadvantages, chief of which was that they were excruciatingly painful. It was rather like putting your hand in the fire to take your mind off the pain of an ingrowing toenail.

Another attempt to deaden pain tried from time to time was more successful and could, had it ever been proved practicable, have done much to lessen suffering before 1846; it still has a place in modern anesthesia. That was the use of ice or snow to numb the part of the body to be operated on. This was first mentioned in the writings of the Persian Avicenna in the eleventh century, referred to again by an Italian, Marco Aurelio Severino, six centuries later, and mentioned still later by the French surgeon Baron Larrey, who noted during Napoleon's disastrous invasion of Russia that wounded soldiers half-frozen by the subzero winter felt little or no pain when he cut off their legs.

Unfortunately, freezing damages or destroys living tissues; furthermore, the results obtained by it were not always satisfactory. The various reports on what we now know as refrigeration anesthesia were never convincing enough to bring it into general use and so the suffering went on and the anguished screams of their tortured patients continued to grate in the ears of the most humane and dedicated surgeons. "Pain," said the distinquished French surgeon Velpeau in 1839, "is the inseparable companion of an operation."

Only seven years later, he was to be proved wrong. On October 16, 1846, the terrible companionship was broken forever and humanity was at last delivered from the pain of surgery. And yet, if man had only had the eyes to see it, the agent of that deliverance had been there waiting to be pressed into service for three centuries, ever since the time of Vesalius.

chapter

3

Aureolus Theophrastus Bombastus von Hohenheim, one of the leading physicians of his day, was born in Switzerland in 1493, at about the same time as his fellow Europeans exploring the New World were having their first frightening experiences with the Indians' "venomous arrowes." Nobly born, he nevertheless spent much of his life wandering from country to country, carousing with such lesser souls as barbers and brothel-keepers, gypsies and "witches"—"in order," he explained, "to understand the wonders of nature."

Paracelsus, as he chose to call himself, was appointed professor of medicine at the University of Basle at the age of thirty-two. There, he built a bonfire of the works of Galen and taught that there was, if only it could be found, a specific remedy for every disease. He is considered by some doctors to be the founder of the modern system of treating illness with drugs. Paracelsus died in 1541 from an injury received in a tavern brawl in Salzburg. Among his manuscripts, long after his death, was found the earliest known account of an experiment with the substance that was to give the world painless surgery: a preparation from alcohol and sulfuric acid called by Paracelsus "sweet vitriol" and known to us by its later name: ether.

Paracelsus gave ether to chickens and found that they fell asleep, but soon awakened unharmed. "In view of the effect of this vitriol," he wrote, "I think it especially noteworthy that its use may be recommended for painful illnesses . . ." Here, for all to see, was the key. Tragically, no one stepped forward to turn it in the lock. Paracelsus offered the world a priceless gift, and the world did not know enough to accept it. There were to be many more near-misses before man eventually triumphed over pain.

In 1800 Sir Humphry Davy, the English genius who illumined the deepest mines with his safety lamp and brought about the marriage of the two sciences of chemistry and electricity, published a book describing some experiments he had carried out with the newly discovered gas nitrous oxide. Davy inhaled the gas and found it had a sweetish taste and a pleasant smell; furthermore, it gave him a great feeling of exhilaration and brought on an overwhelming desire to laugh. He called it "laughing gas," and, having once breathed it when he was nagged by the pain of an aching wisdom tooth, added: "As nitrous oxide in its extensive operation appears capable of destroying physical pain, it may probably be used with advantage during surgical operations . . ." He even suggested the addition of "oxygene or common air" to nitrous oxide to make its inhalation safer.

The combination of nitrous oxide and oxygen, accompanied by an injection of curare (or one of the many drugs with a similar action developed in the laboratory since 1942), is widely used by modern anesthesiologists: it is considered the safest of all methods of anesthesia. Yet not one surgeon of the day recognized the importance of Davy's discovery and tried to apply it in the operating room. Even he himself cannot have grasped its full significance, for he never pursued it any further, even though he was later given a second chance to preside over the conquest of pain.

The year was 1824. A young country surgeon named Henry Hill Hickman, practicing in the picturesque old town of Ludlow, in Shropshire, had discovered that he could cut off puppies' tails painlessly while they were in what he called a state of "suspended animation" from inhaling the fumes of carbon dioxide.

Hickman believed, rightly, that he had made a momentous discovery, one that every surgeon in the world should know about. He wrote to the Royal Society, describing his experiments and seeking their confirmation by the greatest scientists in the land. His letter was ignored, so he published it as a pamphlet. Still no one listened.

The president of the Royal Society at this time was none other than Sir Humphry Davy, now grown rich and famous but still, as a result of his experiments years before, the recognized authority on the inhalation of gases. Hickman, working on his own with no precedents to guide him, had hit on the principle of anesthesia; the agent he used was wrong but he had proved practicable what Davy had only suggested. Had Davy supported him, had he suggested he try nitrous oxide instead of carbon dioxide, the world would have had to wait no longer for its release from pain. Instead, Hickman's work was totally ignored. Six years later, after a futile visit to Paris to try to interest the French Academy of Medicine in his discovery, he died, at the age of thirty, a disappointed man.

The search shifts now to the United States, where once again several men were to stand on the brink of the discovery before it was actually made. Sam Colt, better known for the permanent sleep induced by his famous revolver, might have discovered the temporary sleep of anesthesia had he possessed any medical qualifications to back up the title of "Dr. Coult" which he assumed when he took a "medicine show" on the road in 1832, at the age of eighteen. Sam made money to pay for the patents on his revolver by giving people nitrous oxide to inhale; their giggles and unpredictable antics as they experienced the "exhilaration" noted by Davy were always good for a laugh. But he once gave too much of the gas to half a dozen red Indians and when they collapsed in a deep sleep Sam became scared and never used "laughing gas" again.

A few years later, another traveling showman whose understanding of nitrous oxide was greater than Sam Colt's inspired what would certainly have been the first successful public demonstration of anesthesia had it not been for an extraordinarily bad stroke of luck. "Professor" Gardner Quincy Colton had no degrees but he had studied medicine for a time in New York before setting himself up with a show that included various simple but spectacular chemical experiments, a lecture on "laughing gas" and a demonstration of its hilarious effects on volunteers from among the audience. Listening to Colton's lecture at Hartford, Connecticut, on December 10, 1844, was a local dentist, Horace Wells, a handsome, sensitive young man of twenty-nine. When the time came for the volunteers to sniff the gas and make public fools of themselves, a man named Cooley sitting next to Wells got up and went to the stage.

The dentist no doubt laughed with the rest of the audience as Cooley shouted and waved his arms and staggered about as if he were drunk. But Wells, to his eternal credit, was more observant than the thousands of others who had watched such demonstrations throughout the United States. He noticed that when Cooley ran into a bench, hard enough to bark his shins quite painfully, he did not even flinch. After Cooley had recovered and returned to his seat, Wells asked if he hadn't hurt himself. Cooley did not remember banging into anything but when he pulled up his trousers and looked he discovered his shins were cut and bleeding.

At that moment—though he is not the man to whom the honor eventually went—Horace Wells discovered anesthesia. If a man could cut his shins and not feel it while under the influence of nitrous oxide, why couldn't he have teeth pulled in the same way? The excited Wells went up to speak to Colton as the audience was leaving and asked him just that question. Colton admitted he had never thought of the idea before, but agreed to meet Wells at his office next day with a bag of gas.

In the noblest tradition Wells made himself the guinea pig of his first experiment. We know now that he was not in great danger. But Wells could not have known that—there were tales that men had died from inhaling too much laughing gas. One of his former pupils, Dr. John M. Riggs, for whom the gum ailment Riggs's disease, or pyorrhea, was later named, agreed to help him. "Our agreement," Riggs said later, "was to push the administration to a point hitherto unknown. We knew not whether death or success confronted us."

Fortunately, it was success—though indirectly the experiment was to lead to Wells's death in tragic fashion a few years later. Colton had brought with him a bladder full of nitrous oxide, fitted with a rubber tube and wooden spigot. Wells took the

29

bag on his knees, put the tube in his mouth and breathed deeply. When he judged his patient to be completely insensible, Riggs grasped one of his large back teeth with the forceps, wrestled it to and fro and finally wrenched it out with the familiar crunching sound that had always before been dreaded by dental patients. Throughout the whole procedure, Wells never stirred. When he came round and was shown the tooth he cried: "It's the greatest discovery ever made! I didn't feel it so much as the prick of a pin!"

Immediately Wells made Colton promise to show him how to make the gas. He dashed around town buying the necessary equipment and for the next month sat up late at night among his bubbling retorts, preparing batches of the gas from ammonium nitrate and testing each one on himself. Whenever satisfied, he would give it to one of his patients and by the middle of January he had used nitrous oxide successfully perhaps a dozen times, and unsuccessfully once or twice, a fact he did not hesitate to record. Now he was ready to break his great news. Nitrous oxide, he believed, would not only usher in painless dentistry; it should be used by surgeons thoughout the world, in "the great capital operations."

Surgery without pain! It was a fantastic idea, utterly against all the laws of nature, and the surgeons were not ready to be persuaded. Wells went to Boston, where he had once practiced, and told his fellow dentists—and as many doctors as he could reach—about the wonderful properties of nitrous oxide. Most of them probably thought he was mad. But eventually he was permitted by John Collins Warren, the elder statesman of Boston surgeons, to give a demonstration before a class of students and a handful of doctors at Massachusetts General Hospital.

One of the students volunteered to be subjected to the experiment and settled himself in the plush operating chair. The stage was set for the dramatic proof that would banish the horrors of the torture chamber from the operating room forever. Pain and surgery, the inseparable companions, were to be parted at last. Then, inexplicably, something went wrong and Wells bungled his demonstration.

For many years after 1845, operating in the mouth under general anesthesia presented special difficulties. Wells was shouldering a heavy dual responsibility by acting as anesthesiologist *and* surgeon, particularly in a public demonstration of such importance. Perhaps, in his nervousness, he withdrew the gas bag before his patient was properly anesthetized; or perhaps he took too long to extract the tooth and the effects of the nitrous oxide were already wearing off. At any rate, before he could hold the tooth aloft in triumph, as he had no doubt imagined himself doing, the student groaned.

The boy said afterwards that even though he had groaned, the tooth-pulling had not hurt him. And later experience was to show that patients may be oblivious to pain and yet still stir or cry out while under the influence of an anesthetic. But Wells's demonstration had been ruined and the seeds of his personal doom sown. The audience laughed him off the stage with cries of "Humbug" and the disappointed dentist returned in shame to Hartford.

However, the final conquest of pain was now only a year and a half away—and Wells deserves credit for it as surely as if that first demonstration had succeeded. For among the men he had told about his discovery was one of his former pupils, William Thomas Green Morton. As well as being a dentist Morton had studied at the Harvard Medical School for two years. He was an able, ambitious, aggressive young man, with more persistence, if less originality, than his teacher, Horace Wells.

A few months after the ill-fated Boston demonstration, Morton visited Wells in Hartford and pressed him for more information about nitrous oxide—where could he get it, how should he use it? If the Boston students had not been impressed by Wells's demonstration, Morton evidently had. He was well aware of the fortune awaiting the dentist who could pull teeth without pain, and obviously wanted to experiment with the method himself.

At this point, there enters the story the third man whose ruin was to be caused by his contribution to the discovery of anesthesia. His name was Charles Thomas Jackson, and he was known to both Wells and Morton as a chemist. He was also a respected geologist and a qualified physician—and an entirely unashamed poacher of other men's ideas. Among several inventions for which he attempted to take credit was Samuel Morse's electric telegraph, which he claimed he suggested in a casual conversation aboard a steamship returning from Europe; Morse called him a "monomaniac" and a "wholesale liar."

Jackson's contribution to the discovery of anesthesia was that once, when Morton asked him for some nitrous oxide, he apologized for not having any available but suggested that Morton try sulfuric ether, since their actions were similar. It was not a suggestion that demanded any particular chemical knowledge for since the days of Sam Colt and the other traveling showmen the practice of inhaling ether, as well as "laughing gas," had become a popular pastime: parties held for the purpose were called "ether frolics." Yet ever afterwards, Jackson was to claim that he had been consciously pursuing the miracle that had so far evaded everyone, some method of overcoming the pain of surgery, and that Morton had merely been his agent in the quest.

It was an insupportable claim, but Morton did follow up Jackson's suggestion. He tried ether—on his wife's dog, their goldfish, caterpillars, and finally himself. He was elated by its results, and began to look for an opportunity to use it in his practice. On the evening of September 30, 1846, the opportunity arrived in the person of a patient named Eben Frost, who came to him with a bad tooth and a terror of the pain its extraction would cause him. Morton told Frost he could pull the tooth without him feeling a thing and Frost, though incredulous, was grateful for even a crumb of hope and agreed to the experiment. Morton poured some ether on his handkerchief and held it under Frost's nose until he passed out. Then, in the light of a taper held by his partner, he pulled out the tooth. The luck that Wells had lacked was thus with Morton from the start, since ether explodes when combined in a certain proportion with air and the open flame of the taper could well have been disastrous.

As soon as Frost came round, the farsighted Morton had him sign a certificate testifying that he had felt no pain, thanks to the special "preparation" he had inhaled. Morton intended to make money with this discovery and he saw no reason to tell anyone his "preparation" was merely ether. After a few more experiments, he was ready to take up where his former teacher had left off. He approached John Collins Warren, the stern-faced old surgeon who had sanctioned Wells's original demonstration. Whether Warren was influenced by Eben Frost's testimonial, or whether he had lingering doubts about the cruel reception his students had given Wells, we shall never know. But he agreed to operate on a patient who had been exposed to Morton's "preparation."

The patient Warren chose for the experiment was a frail young printer named Gilbert Abbott who had a tumor on his neck, near the angle of his jaw. At ten o'clock on the morning of October 16, Dr. Warren addressed the customary audience of doctors and students who used to watch his operations, crowded into the banks of seats that rose steeply from the floor of the "surgical pit" under the dome of Massachusetts General Hospital. He told them the history of the case and how he proposed to deal with it. Fifteen minutes later, he had finished his lecture and Abbott had been strapped into the reclining operating chair— but there was no sign of Morton. "As Dr. Morton has not arrived," said Warren icily, "I presume he is otherwise engaged." And he reached for his knife.

At that moment, Morton bustled in. He had decided the ether would be better administered from a glass inhaler than on a handkerchief, and he was hot from the workshop of the craftsman who had just finished making it for him. The glass globe contained a sponge saturated with ether and had two openings in the top—one to admit air and the other fitted with a tube to be put in the patient's mouth. With Morton, who did not believe in taking chances, was Eben Frost, his living testimonial in case this demonstration, too, was a failure.

Dr. Warren listened courteously as Morton apologized for being late and then told him: "Well, sir, your patient is ready." Morton was a burly man with a flowing mustache and on this day he was wearing a flamboyant patterned waistcoat in jaunty contrast with Warren's sober frock coat. His appearance evidently inspired confidence in Abbott, for the young man seemed unafraid as Morton told him how to take the tube of the inhaler in his mouth and breathe deeply through it. The secret "preparation," he said, would completely blot out the pain of the knife; there—gesturing toward Frost—was a man who had tried it. And Frost nodded his confirmation. Abbott followed Morton's instructions and took the tube in his mouth. Even though he was bound to the chair, his body twitched and his arms jerked spasmodically as he slipped into unconsciousness, struggles that were to become familiar to later generations of anesthesiologists. Morton held the tube in his patient's mouth until he was still and his

33

breathing was deep and regular. Then, with a confidence verging on insolence, the unknown dentist told the eminent surgeon: "Sir, *your* patient is ready."

The watching doctors and students craned forward in their seats. Warren grasped the tumor in his left hand; his right, with a practiced sweep of flashing steel, laid open the flesh. This was the hated moment his lifetime in the operating room had taught him to accept, the moment when the despairing screams would break over his head in a wave of protesting torment. This time, the screams never came. Swiftly he worked on in the unnatural silence, slicing around the tumor, separating it from the surrounding tissues, tying off the blood vessels, stitching up the wound. Once, Abbott stirred slightly and mumbled a few unintelligible sounds, but by this time Warren had almost finished. As his patient slowly returned to consciousness, the old surgeon bent down and asked him urgently if he had felt any pain. Not really, the printer replied—perhaps just a sort of blunt scratching on his cheek.

John Collins Warren must certainly now have remembered that other demonstration months before. For he straightened up, faced his audience, and said, with an echo of the jeers that had driven Horace Wells from this same room: "Gentlemen, this is no humbug."

In a few historic minutes the tyranny of pain had been overthrown. Anesthesia, the greatest discovery of the age, was no longer the ridiculous dream of a couple of obscure dentists but a triumphant, merciful fact. Surgery had been freed from its "inseparable" partner, even though the divorce had taken what seems an unnecessarily long time—it was now three centuries since Paracelsus had recommended "sweet vitriol" for "painful illnesses," and forty-six years since Humphry Davy had suggested that "laughing gas" might be used "with advantage" during surgical operations.

Why should the world have had to wait so long for such an obvious blessing? There can be only one answer, strange as it must seem. Pain had haunted man since his beginning; he accepted it as he accepted other manifestations of nature, with no spirit of revolt. Pain was the will of God, as inevitable as the closing in of night at the end of the day. Surely only a madman would rebel against the night?

34

How else is it possible to explain the most incredibly missed opportunity in the whole extraordinary story of the introduction of anesthesia? For when John Collins Warren operated on Gilbert Abbott it was not the first time a tumor had been removed under the influence of ether. It had been done before—four years before—in the little southern farming village of Jefferson, Georgia. On March 30, 1842, a Jefferson doctor named Crawford Williamson Long sprinkled ether on a towel, held it to the nose of a patient named James Venable, and then cut a tumor from the back of his neck. Venable felt no pain—and Crawford Williamson Long, two years earlier even than the ill-fated Horace Wells, stood for a moment on the threshold of fame. Astonishingly, he failed to realize the significance of what he had done. He had overcome pain in this one case but apparently the idea that pain could be permanently excluded from the operating room never occurred to him. He made no effort to arouse the enthusiasm of others nor did he bother to pursue his discovery himself. He used ether only four or five times during the next four years and wrote no paper about it until 1849—three years after Morton had been hailed as a savior of mankind.

By this time, the three men who had contributed most directly to the introduction of anesthesia had become locked in a squalid controversy that eventually brought about their destruction.

The first victim was Horace Wells. Wells had gone on using nitrous oxide in his dental practice even after his disastrous demonstration in Boston. He knew it worked, and so did his grateful patients, but Morton's success where he had failed seemed to unhinge him. He wrote to various publications advancing his claim to be considered the true father of painless surgery without success. And he experimented on himself more furiously than ever with his own nitrous oxide, with ether, and with a new anesthetic agent that was becoming popular in Europe, chloroform.

Sadly, it is not uncommon for doctors to fall victim to the drugs they prescribe for others. Wells became addicted to his anesthetics. His health as well as his mental stability now undermined, he abandoned his wife and child in Hartford and went to New York. There, on a January evening in 1848—perhaps while his senses were befuddled from breathing chloroform—he threw acid on the coat of a strolling prostitute and was arrested.

From his prison cell he wrote a poignant letter to his wife in which he said: "I feel I am fast becoming deranged . . ." Then he tied a chloroform-soaked handkerchief around his mouth, breathed deeply several times and as his consciousness ebbed away slashed open the great artery in his thigh with a straight-edged razor and bled to death. Anesthesia had brought him nothing but grief and tragedy, but at least at the end it eased his passing.

Neither Morton nor Jackson ever admitted any indebtedness to Wells. His death left them free to continue their sordid squabble over which one of them deserved credit for the discovery, a squabble which began within weeks of Gilbert Abbott's operation and continued with growing virulence for many years. From the first, Morton had behaved with considerably less altruism than one expects in a benefactor of mankind. He had always attempted to disguise the fact that his secret "preparation" was simply ether. He called it "Letheon" and added other substances to it to change its color and smell. Within two weeks of his triumphant demonstration he had filed an application for a patent on his "invention" in his name and Jackson's, though Jackson agreed to assign his interest in it to Morton for ten percent of the proceeds—surprising generosity in a man who was later to claim sole credit for the discovery. By licensing doctors in various areas to use "Letheon," Morton hoped to make at least half a million dollars, and he actually did manage to sell some franchises. But when the surgeons at the Massachusetts General Hospital refused to continue using "Letheon" unless he told them what it was he had to confess that it was only ether, and his patent was subsequently never renewed.

Unworthy though his quest for riches may have been, it is difficult not to sympathize with Morton. For, to compound his frustrations, even the public adulation he at first enjoyed was soon tempered by Jackson's machinations. Within a few months of Morton's demonstration, which he had not even attended, Jackson wrote a paper for delivery to the American Academy of Arts and Sciences in which he managed to proclaim himself the discoverer of anesthesia without even mentioning Morton's name. Then he sent a newspaper account of the speech which seemed to convey the Academy's acceptance of his claim to a friend in Paris, asking him to announce the discovery to the

French Academy of Sciences. In this way, at least temporarily, he managed to convince most of Europe that the real honor was his.

The ugly dispute raged on for years. At one time, a bill was introduced in Congress proposing that Morton be awarded $100,000 in recognition of his achievement. Incensed, Jackson hired a lawyer to lobby for him in Washington and when partisans of first Wells and then Crawford Long also entered the lists the waters became so muddied that the bill was dropped. Morton battled on fruitlessly for twenty-two years, exhausting whatever money he had made from his discovery and sinking so deeply into debt that his house was seized. Eventually his health broke down and he died of a stroke in July 1868, a few weeks short of his forty-ninth birthday. Jackson continued the controversy for five more years—until he was committed to an insane asylum, where he died seven years later.

Only Crawford Long remained as untouched by tragedy as he had been by the significance of the operation he performed on James Venable in 1842. After running a Confederate hospital during the Civil War, he returned to his practice and died in 1878, at the age of sixty-two, suffering a stroke just after he had delivered a baby—to a woman whose labor pangs he had eased with ether.

Though anesthesia never made William Morton the fortune he coveted, he lived long enough, which must have been at best a doubtful consolation to him, to see its use become universal in the hospitals of America and Europe. But anesthesia was not an end, it was a beginning—the beginning of the spectacular emergence of surgery from the darkness in which it had dwelt for thousands of years. And this Morton was not to see. For before it could be achieved there was a second great battle to be fought.

Ether was first used in a surgical operation in Europe two months after Dr. Warren operated on Gilbert Abbott's tumor. The Scottish giant Robert Liston used it to amputate the diseased leg of a London butler named Frederick Churchill with, as he wrote that same evening, "the most perfect and satisfactory results." Liston was so swift and skillful with the knife that his operations were always watched by an alert and admiring audience of students who used to joke that if they blinked while he was at work they risked missing an amputation. Among the students watching him use ether before cutting off Churchill's leg, with a speed that was ever afterwards to be unnecessary, was a tall, grave youth of nineteen with a shy stammer, Joseph Lister. The son of a prosperous Quaker wine merchant, Joseph Lister was destined to become perhaps the greatest surgeon of all time. And his supreme achievement was to be his conquest of the second mortal enemy barring surgery's progress: infection.

John Collins Warren and Robert Liston were at the peak of their profession, but in one vital respect they knew no more than the shaggiest caveman opening skulls in the Stone Age: they had no idea of the necessity for cleanliness in surgery. And neither did any other surgeon of their day, or for years to come.

If a surgeon in the first half of the nineteenth century bothered to wash his hands or instruments at all, it would probably be after the operation not before it. He was quite likely to strop his knife on his boot and hold it between his teeth until he needed it. Surgeons kept special coats for operating—cast-off frock coats which were never washed but were allowed to accumulate caked layers of pus and dried blood, the thickness of which testified to the wealth of the wearer's experience. Conditions in the wards to which the patients were moved after the operation were, if possible, even more ghastly. In the worst hospitals, beds in which patients had died from highly infectious diseases were used over and over again without any attempt to wash the sheets—if indeed the bags of straw or wood shavings used as mattresses were ever graced by the presence of sheets.

Submitting to surgery under these conditions was like playing Russian roulette with only one blank cartridge in the revolver chamber. If the pain of the operation did not kill the unfortunate patient, his wound was almost certain to become infected. The formation of pus in a wound was welcomed as evidence that a more dangerous infection had been staved off. Terrible forms of blood poisoning and other infections ran riot through the wards, the worst of them being known as "hospital gangrene," a disease in which the patient's body literally rotted away. A gray mass of dead tissue would encrust the outside of the wound and beneath it the disease would make its insidious invasion of the healthy parts of the body. First to go would be the soft tissue separating the muscles, which would sometimes be so con-

38

sumed that a man could slide his hand between two living muscles. Next the muscles themselves would be attacked, and gradually even the blood vessels would disintegrate. It was a horrible fate, and anyone who underwent surgery risked it.

The heavy stench of death hanging over hospital wards prompted the Scottish surgeon James Young Simpson to say: "A man laid on the operating table in one of our surgical hospitals is exposed to more chance of death than was the English soldier on the field of Waterloo." He did not know why, but perhaps he was groping toward an understanding of the problem when he suggested that hospitals be built of iron instead of brick so that they could be dismantled and moved from time to time.

American hospitals had a better record than their European counterparts, but between 1830 and 1860 in Pennsylvania 24.3 percent of all patients undergoing amputations died. At the Massachusetts General Hospital, the rate was 26 percent. In Paris at around the same time, the death rate after amputation was 58.8 percent. Operations within the abdomen were seldom performed before anesthesia, but whenever they were, the death rate was even more horrifying. In England, 86 percent of the women subjected to Caesarean section died.

The most minor injury or surgical operation was as likely to become infected as the major ones; as long as the skin was broken, the danger was there. The standard treatment for a compound fracture of the leg, or arm, one in which the broken bone protrudes through the skin, was to amputate the limb to prevent blood poisoning. And yet the operation itself was just as likely to cause infection as the original injury—perhaps even more likely, because of the deplorable lack of hygiene in hospitals. Joseph Lister earned immortality by ending this tragic toll of hospital-inflicted suffering and death. And by coincidence—since it was his father's dealings in wine that paid for his medical studies—he conquered infection by applying to medicine the lessons learned in the study of wine by another pioneer, the French chemist Louis Pasteur.

Called upon to discover why some batches of wine were being spoiled, Pasteur traced the cause to an invasion by tiny living organisms—bacteria—present in the air. He found that when these organisms were killed by heat—the process still known as pasteurization—the wine remained pure. Lister had already con-

39

cluded that somehow or other mere contact with the air was enough to cause infection, since while compound fractures virtually always became infected, ordinary ones, in which the skin remained unbroken, healed without any trouble. When a friend told him about Pasteur's work, Lister immediately realized that the same invisible organisms which were spoiling the wine were probably responsible for the infection of wounds.

But how to combat them? He could not, obviously, apply enough heat to a wound to "pasteurize" it. He cast around for some chemical substance that would achieve the same result, and the one he chose was carbolic acid. He had seen it being used to disinfect sewage in the English town of Carlisle, in a dark, tarry form known as German creosote. And so he smeared this unappetizing substance on wounds. Miraculously, it seemed, they healed without becoming infected. But the harsh creosote also damaged the flesh tissues so, by a patient process of trial and error, Lister tried purified carbolic acid, diluted first in water, then in various oils.

Gradually he worked out the details of his campaign against poisoning—"antisepsis." Some hours before he operated, Lister had lint soaked in carbolized oil placed on the patient's skin to cleanse it; he dipped his knife in carbolic before beginning to cut; he drenched the wound with carbolic before stitching it up; then he covered it with carbolic dressings. Instead of dying, his patients recovered, and in 1867 he published his news to the medical world. Doctors were not as quick to seize on his discovery as they had been to recognize the blessings of anesthesia. One said he preferred to attribute infection to Providence, rather than to tiny organisms he could not even see. But eventually Lister's success in eliminating infection from his wards convinced the doubters.

Their hands no longer tied by the twin restraints of pain and infection, surgeons were now able to develop operations which had hitherto been far beyond their powers. Anesthesia ended the race against the clock and gave them time to devise better ways of accomplishing existing operations, as well as the opportunity to discover entirely new ones. Antisepsis meant that their patients recovered instead of being carted off to a filthy ward to die.

In 1874 the respected British surgeon Sir John Erichsen pointed out that the art of surgery, like any other art, could only be carried to a certain point of excellence. "The abdomen, the chest, and the brain," he said, "will be for ever shut from the intrusion of the wise and humane surgeon." Sir John was a good surgeon but a poor prophet. Within a quarter of a century, wise and humane surgeons were carrying out with impunity operations for which, in the words of a contemporary observer, they would have been prosecuted a generation earlier. By the turn of the century surgeons had not only intruded into the abdomen but had cut out and removed the stomach; they had penetrated the chest and removed a lung; they had even invaded the most complex of all our organs and removed a brain tumor.

The spectacular success of these bold ventures into the unknown, the seemingly miraculous way in which they saved the lives or relieved the sufferings of innumerable patients who had always before been deemed incurable, overshadowed for many years the development of the infant medical science which had first made them possible, anesthesia. A few drops of ether or chloroform poured onto a sponge or cloth and held beneath a patient's nose enabled him to sleep through the pain of an operation; that was enough for most surgeons. How best could anesthetics be given? What was the safe dosage? How long could a patient safely be kept under anesthesia? What unseen harmful effects did it have? Even the questions occurred to only a handful of doctors; fewer still bothered to try to discover the answers.

Occasionally a patient would take a few whiffs of an anesthetic and suddenly collapse and die, before the surgeon had made his first incision. Or he would appear to tolerate the operation, only to die hours or days later. What had killed him—his condition, the operation, or the anesthetic? The answer was considered unimportant. Such infrequent accidents were widely accepted as a small price to pay for the tremendous advances anesthesia had made possible. But they prompted a few doctors to begin investigating the mysteries of this strange phenomenon called anesthesia, a physical process so complex that it is not yet thoroughly understood. Gradually the slapdash methods of the early days were superseded. That new medical specialist, the anesthesiologist, took his place at the head of the patient laid on the operating table. New gases were added to his armory. New drugs were introduced which further refined his art.

41

The most important of all these new drugs, the dreaded arrow poison curare, did not arrive in the operating room until almost a century after Morton. But when it came, it brought with it revolutionary changes—changes as important to the development and improvement of anesthesia as anesthesia itself had been to surgery so many years before.

part

2

chapter

4

How and when the first hunter learned to increase the deadliness of his arrows or spears by dipping them in poison must remain as much of a mystery as the origin of the wheel. Perhaps, in his endless rovings in search of food, some skin-clad caveman crouched behind a tree and watched an animal paralyzed by the bite of a snake and then, with man's characteristic facility for exploiting his fellow creatures, resolved to catch a snake and use the venom himself. Or, knowing that certain berries made him ill if he ate them, he may have decided by some primitive groping toward scientific experiment to see if their juice would similarly harm his prey and hinder its attempts to flee. We shall never know, but it is certain that there are few parts of the world where poisoned weapons have not been used at some time in history, both in hunting and in war.

Spears dating back more than twenty-five thousand years, to the last Ice Age, have been found in what is now Germany. Their blades, fashioned out of bone, bear notches or grooves thought to have carried poison into the wounds they inflicted. Arrows with similar hollows have been found in prehistoric caves among the Pyrenees, in southwest France. The earliest written reference to arrow poisons was made during the Vedic period in India, which began fifteen centuries before Christ. Ancient Sanskrit writings of this period refer to a law banning the use of "secret weapons," including barbs on spears and poisoned arrows.

The Scythians, a belligerent tribe of nomadic horsemen who established themselves on the Black Sea in what is now the Crimea, nine centuries before Christ, were dreaded not only for their skill with the bow but for the snake venom, mixed with human blood, which they painted on their arrows. Thus armed, they successfully invaded the Assyrian empire, Palestine, and part of the Balkan peninsula. Alexander the Great mounted an unsuccessful expedition against them and lost some of his men to their arrows.

The Greeks considered the Scythians deplorable barbarians but the Greek word for a bow, *toxon,* is thought to have derived from the Scythian *takhsha.* That there was a close association between bows and arrows and poison in those days is shown by the fact that a variety of modern words for poison and poisoning—"toxin," "toxic," "intoxication," and the rest—developed from the same Greek root. The original meaning of "bow" survives in the word "toxophily," the sport of archery.

Poisoned arrows are mentioned several times in classical literature. Homer spoke of Odysseus "seeking the deadly drug wherewith to anoint his arrows" and Vergil, centuries later, wrote of a character highly skilled "in tincturing darts and arming steel with poison." Horace and Ovid, among others, also referred to the poisoning of weapons and Pliny commented, "What other animal besides man immerses his arms in poison . . . Do we realize our guilt?"

Whether the guilt was realized or not, the practice continued in Europe for centuries. The Celts and the Gauls poisoned their arrows, as did other European peoples, particularly the Franks, a group of warlike Germanic tribes living along the Rhine who were united in the fifth century A.D. into an empire which eventually encompassed present-day France, the Low Countries, much of Germany, Austria, Switzerland, and the northern and central parts of Italy. The Franks richly deserved the description of barbarians. They fought interminably among themselves and were sufficiently familiar with poisoned arms to induce a malevolent

46

queen named Fredegunde, wife of a deposed king, to hire a couple of servants to stab the new king, Sigibert, with poisoned knives.

This sort of private toxicological enterprise was frowned upon, and fines were stipulated for it in Frankish laws in the seventh and eighth centuries, but the use of poisoned weapons in hunting and even warfare continued for many years. They are said to have been used in the twelfth century, in fighting between Germans and Serbs in what is now Yugoslavia, and in 1552, in a war between Henry II of France and Charles I of Spain. As late as 1675, it was considered advisable to outlaw poisoned arms in a form of early Geneva convention drawn up by France and Germany.

It is not known how many types of arrow poison existed in early Europe or exactly how they were made. Snake venom was undoubtedly included in some recipes, either alone or mixed with blood or poisons extracted from plants. Most common of the plant poisons was probably juice from the roots of aconite, or wolf's bane, a hardy perennial found in some gardens under the name of monkshood. This plant has pretty blue, purple, yellow, or white flowers shaped like hoods, but the juice of its root, if it finds its way into the bloodstream, causes first stomach ache, then weakness and dizziness, followed by loss of consciousness and convulsions, difficulty in breathing, and, if the dose is large enough, death. Aconite slows the action of the heart and though too dangerous to have much value it has been prescribed by doctors to lower blood pressure and as a sedative.

Another plant with toxic properties that may have been a constituent of the European arrow poisons is a form of hellebore known by the botanical name *Veratrum album*. Around the turn of the century, an indefatigable German researcher named Louis Lewin injected juice from a hellebore plant into a cat, which died in convulsions fifty-four minutes later. Lewin spent thirty years of his life studying the history of poisoned weapons and subjecting animals ranging in size from guinea pigs to horses to the effects of poisons supplied to him by museums and botanical gardens around the world. In 1923 he published the results of his research in a monumental work called *Die Pfeilgifte* (The Arrow Poisons) which detailed innumerable toxic mixtures of

47

plant and animal substances used at one time or another by hunters or warriors on all five continents.

While the advance of civilization—or more probably the adoption of firearms—ended the era of poisoned weapons in Europe, their use went on elsewhere in the world. Lewin tells the story that in India, when the Mongol conqueror Tamerlane was advancing on Delhi in 1398, its defenders tied poisoned spears to the tusks of elephants and drove them out to meet the foe. The ingenious Tamerlane countered by ordering flaming torches tied to the horns of buffaloes, which fearsome prospect stampeded the elephants and enabled him to capture the city.

Three centuries later, strange reports began to circulate in Europe about a fantastic tree growing in southeast Asia—reports curiously similar to the legends about curare which had long been drifting back from South America. This alarming tree, called the Upas in Java and the Ipoh by the people of the Malay peninsula, was said to give off such potent emanations that any creature straying near it, man or animal, promptly died. No grass grew for ten miles around a Upas tree, and even birds unlucky enough to fly over it fell from the skies as if hit by an arrow. Its sap was so poisonous that if it came into contact with the slightest scratch on a man's hand he would die within seconds, and half an hour later his body would have rotted away.

Such a formidable tree soon attracted more sober investigation and an Englishman named Stevens dispelled the legends about it, to his own satisfaction at least, by climbing up into its branches for a picnic lunch. He also slept the night under the tree and stuck his head in the steam rising from a bucket of its boiling sap for an hour without incurring the slightest ill effect from the mysterious vapors.

But the legends were not altogether unjustified, for the milky sap of the Upas tree (*Antiaris toxicaria*), a member of the mulberry family, contains a virulent poison called antiarin which was first isolated in France in 1824. The distinguished French physiologist François Magendie found that six drops of the active principle of *Antiaris toxicaria* were enough to kill a dog or a cat—a fact which had not escaped generations of tribes in the areas where the Upas grows, since they slashed grooves in the tree, collected the sap, concentrated it over fires, and smeared it on their arrowheads. Monkeys wounded by these arrows died within a

48

couple of minutes. More research in Europe showed that the poison had a violent effect on the heart, and attempts were made to take advantage of this by administering minute doses to patients whose hearts beat too weakly. It was rejected, however, as too dangerous—though half a seed of the Upas tree taken three times daily was once a favorite Indian remedy for fever.

Medical science was to benefit much more from a poison used by hunters in parts of tropical Africa. The nineteenth-century Scottish missionary David Livingstone found that some of the tribes he visited during his exploration of the eastern part of Africa, south of the equator, coated their spears with a poison so potent it enabled them to kill elephants. Dr. Livingstone reported that they obtained this poison by pulverizing the tiny seeds of a trailing vine into a sticky pulp. He identified the vine as a member of the large *Strophanthus* family, which includes garden plants like the periwinkle and the oleander. Scientists have since extracted several valuable drugs from varieties of *Strophanthus* growing in many different areas of the world. From the variety Dr. Livingstone reported, they isolated a drug called strophanthin with a similar effect to digitalis (another plant poison extracted from a familiar garden flower, the foxglove), which has a strongly stimulating effect on the heart and is invaluable in treating some forms of heart disease.

Strophanthin itself proved too dangerous for use in all but the greatest emergencies, but later one of its close relatives, a shrub called *Strophanthus gratus*—also used as an arrow poison —yielded another heart-stimulating drug called ouabain with a more controllable life-saving action, and ouabain is widely prescribed in modern medicine.

The plant kingdom was not the only storehouse of materials for the primitive poison-makers. Snake venom was used by many other peoples besides the ancient Scythians, and the stings of scorpions figured in some formulas. So did the poisons, or even the whole bodies, of other venomous insects, animals, and fish. Some of these substances are still used today in remote areas of the world where isolated tribes hunt their food in the old way.

Australian aborigines make an arrow poison from the crushed larvae of a type of locust. The adult locust is not poisonous, but its larval stage is, and if injected into an animal's bloodstream it can break down the red corpuscles. Poisonous leeches were

49

used in a similar way by some tribes in Malaya until recent times. Several varieties of tropical fish have poisonous spikes or barbs on their backs, and these were broken off and fitted to the tips of arrows.

The Cholo Indians living in the rain forests sandwiched between the Andes and the Pacific coast of Colombia dip their blowgun darts even today in a poison exuded by the skin of a small, yellow-striped black frog. A single frog—its Indian name is *kokoa*—can yield enough poison to arm fifty darts, and animals wounded by them soon die in convulsions. Scientists call this frog *Phyllobates latinasus* and from its venom they have isolated one of the most highly toxic substances known to man.

Smearing arrows with a sort of "ointment" made from putrefying flesh was another unpleasant method of trying to increase their effectiveness employed in various parts of the world. The Melanesian tribesmen of the New Hebrides, a group of islands in the South Pacific east of Australia, prepared a diabolical poison right up to modern times. They would fashion an arrow tip from human bone and then stick it in the decomposing flesh of a human corpse for seven to eight days. After that they would coat it with earth found in only one special place—earth which was later analyzed and found to be rich in the bacilli that cause tetanus, a fearsome disease with a later place in the curare story. Sometimes, instead of the earth, they would rub the arrows in the excrement of crabs. A guinea pig that Lewin had poisoned with one of these mixtures died six days later in the convulsions of tetanus.

A variation of the decomposing-flesh technique was used by the Dakota Indians before the white man arrived in the American west. They would pin down a rattlesnake with a forked stick and allow it to sink its fangs repeatedly into the liver of a deer. The liver would then be wrapped in hide and buried for a week to rot, after which it would be dried, mixed with blood, and left to dry again. A paste made from the poisoned liver was used in warfare as well as hunting.

Two other poisons made by some tribes in the western United States, but used only for hunting, contained formic acid from the stings of bees and red ants. These mixtures were not fatal to hunted animals, but they made wounds so painful that the animal, instead of taking flight, would often writhe in agony trying to bite out the poison, making it much easier to capture.

Throughout history, whether on long-forgotten battlefields of ancient Europe or in remote jungles where naked tribes still live almost untouched by the modern world, arrow poisons have killed or tormented their victims in a variety of ways. Some—the most potent—had a devastating effect on the heart. Some affected the nerves. Many, probably, did not kill until days later, and then only because the wounds through which they gained access to the body were more likely than most to become infected.

But in the whole sinister arsenal of arrow poisons none was as swift, as mysterious, or as sure in its effects as curare, the "flying death." And none was destined to make such a valuable contribution to the welfare of humanity.

chapter

5

The first white man to fall to curare was probably a member of Columbus's second expedition to the Americas in 1493. A book published in London in 1553, based on the writings of the German monk and geographer Sebastian Münster, described a clash that took place on one of the Caribbean islands between Columbus's men and cannibals, "with whom our men, bickering, left one of their companions, by reason that these barbarians are accustomed to infect their arrows with venom."

So soon did the adventure which had started out peaceably and with such high hopes begin to go sour. The explorers' first impressions of the Americas were of great natural beauty and riches. They rejoiced at the magnificent landscape of the Caribbean islands and rhapsodized over the extravagant tropical vegetation and jewel-like birds. Many were the marvels described by Friar Martyr. In the Indies, he said, there were huge rivers of pure gold and emeralds as big as goose eggs; islands whose only inhabitants were women, as complaisant as women in those circumstances might be expected to be; a spring whose water "maketh owld men younge ageyne." It was all too idyllic to last. The cruelties soon to be perpetrated by the Spaniards, their plunder of the peoples they found living in the huge continent of South America, made a tragic contrast with the earlier hopes.

Martyr himself never visited the magical lands of which he wrote, though his book was no more fantastic than the works of some travelers who had seen its wonders with their own eyes. Before leaving Italy for the court of Queen Isabella he had risen to a position of some eminence in the church, and his book is based on letters he sent back to Rome recounting the exploits of the conquistadors. Called *The Decades of the New World,* it begins with the journeys of Columbus and extends over the subsequent twenty or so years. He gathered his material by eagerly listening to any returned traveler who could be persuaded to accept the hospitality of his table. "Not one of those who came to court," he said, "failed to offer me the pleasure, whether verbally or in writing, of reporting to me everything he had learned."

Early in his book he describes a touching meeting with the inhabitants of Hispaniola on Columbus's first voyage. Startled by their first sight of white men, the natives fled in consternation, but the Spaniards managed to capture one woman. They took her back to their ships where, "filling her with meat and wine, and appareling her, they let her depart to her company." Shortly after, "a great multitude of them came running to the shore to behold this new nation whom they thought to have descended from heaven. They cast themselves by heaps into the sea and came swimming to the ships, bringing gold with them, which they changed with our men for earthen pots, drinking glasses, pins, hawk's bells and such other trifles."

Gold! Here was the root of so much later evil, and the Spaniards soon ceased to give even earthen pots or pins in exchange for it; they simply took it wherever they found it. "We came here to serve God and the king, and also to get rich," said Bernal Díaz del Castillo, one of the conquerors of Mexico, who boasted that he had fought in more than a hundred battles and skirmishes against the inhabitants of the New World. The Indians retaliated with the only weapon they had, curare. Discoverers and discovered died in their thousands and savagery reigned on both sides. The Aztecs sacrificed Spanish prisoners to the god of war before the eyes of their comrades and Vasco Núñez de Balboa, discoverer of the Pacific and one of the most humane of the conquistadors, was not above throwing prisoners to the fierce mastiffs and hounds that accompanied the Spaniards on their conquests.

Martyr describes an engagement typical in its ferocity. Balboa came upon a "native king" at the head of an army of naked warriors, called upon him to stop, and attacked when he failed to obey the order. Six hundred of the warriors were "slayne like brute beasts." Martyr writes: "Oure men, following them in the chase, hewed them in pieces as the butchers do flesh . . . from one an arm, from another a leg, from him a buttock . . ." and so on. Balboa later discovered that the king's court was "infected with the most abominable and unnatural lechery, for he found the king's brother and many other young men in women's apparel, smooth and effeminately decked." The standard-bearers of Christ obviously could not permit such a flouting of sexual morality to go unpunished and Balboa had about forty of the young homosexuals "given for a prey to his dogges."

The wrath of the conquistadors was a terrible thing. Martyr tells how one of the boldest of the Spanish captains, Alonso de Ojeda, once "invaded, slew and spoiled" the people of a village on an island in the southern Caribbean "because they had been before time cruel against the Christians and could never be allured to permit them quietly to come within their dominions." Having sacked the village and looted its gold, Ojeda forced his prisoners to guide him twelve miles inland to another village where some of the Indians were supposed to have fled. There was a furious battle and one of Ojeda's lieutenants and fifty of his men were killed by arrows "infected with the deadly poison of a certain herb." Ojeda retired to his ship, where he was soon joined by another captain, Diego Nicuesa, and five more ships. Thus reinforced, he took a landing party of several hundred men back to the village, surrounded it, and set its hundred or so houses on fire, "with diligent watch that none might escape." As Martyr wrote: "In short time they brought them and their houses to ashes and made them pay the ransom of blood for blood."

Ojeda then sailed to the mainland and set about building a fortress. Some of the Indian prisoners he took on this foray told him there was a village a short way inland which had a rich gold mine, and he promptly determined to loot it. But he was beaten off, "for these people also use bows and venomous ar-

54

rows." A few days later, "being enforced for lack of victuals to invade another village," Ojeda himself was "stricken in the thigh with an arrow." Martyr, an inveterate gossip, suggests that the arrow might have been fired in revenge by a man whose wife Ojeda had taken captive. Months later, Ojeda died on the island of Hispaniola, "tossed and turmoiled with tempests and vexed with a thousand perplexities . . . by the force of the poison of his venomous wound."

That he lived so long after being wounded shows that whatever it was he died from, it was not curare. More likely, his wound became infected and he died from blood poisoning. Many different recipes are used to prepare curare in the jungles of South America but the poison always has the same action: it paralyzes the voluntary muscles, those muscles over which we have conscious control. It has no effect on involuntary muscles, such as the heart. Death occurs when the curare, carried round the body by the blood, reaches the muscles controlling breathing. If the dose is large enough, the victim dies within minutes. If it is too small to be fatal, the poison does not affect the respiratory muscles and whatever degree of paralysis is caused in other muscles soon wears off, as the body's natural defenses surround and neutralize the invading drug.

Within a minute or so of being wounded, the curare victim begins to feel dizzy. His eye muscles are the first to be overtaken by the paralysis and he finds it difficult to focus clearly. Then his jaws go slack. His eyelids droop and before they close completely he is seeing double. He struggles to cry out, perhaps, but all that escapes his throat is a strange, animal-like whimpering as one after the other his lips, his tongue, and his vocal cords lapse into immobility. Soon all the muscles of his face go limp and it becomes as still and expressionless as a death mask. Now he loses the power to move his legs and arms, though his fingers may still twitch in a futile effort to express his panic at the overpowering sensation of choking he feels as the muscles of his throat are attacked and he loses his ability to swallow. Then it is the turn of the larger muscles, in his back and his abdomen. Finally, the poison reaches and stills the muscles of his chest and his diaphragm, his lungs cease to move, and death ends his ordeal.

How long he takes to die depends on the strength of the curare and how much of it has entered his bloodstream. It can be five minutes, or fifteen, twenty, or even longer. The horror of curare is that however long it takes to kill, its victim remains conscious until he suffocates. He knows what is happening to him and he can still hear what is happening around him, though he cannot in the later stages make any sound himself. He can still feel heat or cold—and pain.

The great French physiologist and scientific investigator Claude Bernard carried out a classic series of experiments with curare in the middle years of the nineteenth century. He wrote: "Within the motionless body, behind the staring eye, with all the appearance of death, feeling and intelligence persist in all their force. Could one conceive of a more horrible suffering than that of an intelligence witnessing the successive subtraction of all the organs that serve it, and thus finding itself enclosed alive within a corpse?" Bernard recalled that poets throughout the ages had evoked their readers' pity with tales of living beings imprisoned in inanimate objects. He mentioned the Italian poet Tasso's story of the beautiful maiden doomed to spend her life in a cypress tree. There are many other examples—few children have not shuddered in sympathy with a prince transformed by a witch into a frog. "The torture invented by the imagination of poets is produced in nature by the action of this American poison," wrote Bernard. He based his vivid picture of the living death inflicted by curare on his careful observations of its action on animals, but we know it is a true one from the experiences of volunteers who have been injected with the drug in modern times.

In 1945 an English medical researcher named Frederick Prescott undertook to be the "guinea pig" in a series of experiments designed to establish the most effective dose of curare for use in anesthesia. On three separate occasions, in Westminster Hospital, London, he received progressively larger doses of the drug. The third dose was large enough to paralyze all his muscles, including those governing his breathing, but he reported afterwards that he remained perfectly aware of what was going on until he began to lose consciousness. He could also feel pain as strips of adhesive plaster were torn from hairy parts of his body. Dr. Prescott was not in danger of dying, since by then the action of the drug was much better understood and his breathing was supported under the supervision of one of England's leading anesthesiologists, Dr. Geoffrey Organe. Nevertheless, twenty-one years later the memory of the experiment was still so unpleasant that Dr. Prescott told me: "The experience was really terrifying, and one I would never repeat again."

This, then, was the ugly death lurking in the hail of arrows which greeted early travelers in South America. It is not surprising that so many fables grew up around so terrible a poison. One early writer says that to test the potency of a new batch of curare it was placed near a cut made in an animal's leg: if the blood immediately began to flow back into the wound, the poison was strong enough for use. Another writer, as late as 1770, reported that an Indian carrying a baby died after being struck by a poisoned arrow. The child was not wounded— but it began to swell and shortly afterwards it, too, died. It is a gruesome tale but it deserves no more credence than the same writer's assertion that in Guiana there was a race of black people whose hands consisted of merely a thumb and a forefinger forked like the claws of a lobster.

The Indians themselves regarded curare as a thing of magic. According to one tribal legend, the ancients had been led to discover the secret of making it by watching sparrow hawks scratch their talons on the bark of a certain tree before pursuing their prey.

Friar Martyr says in one place that the arrow poison was made from "the juice of a death-dealing herb." Elsewhere he mentions "the juice they distil from certain trees," supplemented by the stings of scorpions, the heads of poisonous ants, and juice pressed from "little plums." The lianas from which curare comes are neither herbs nor trees, but another chronicler of the Spanish conquest who, unlike Martyr, took part in it himself, may have come nearer the truth. In 1526 Gonzalo Fernández de Oviedo y Valdés published a book called *The Natural History of the West Indies,* in which he wrote: "The apples wherewith the Indian cannibals envenom their arrows grow on certain trees covered with many branches and leaves being very green and growing thick. They are laden with an abundance of these evyll frutes . . ." This reference to apples is puzzling since the liana from which one of the most potent forms of curare is prepared does bear fruit which might be mistaken for apples, though it is the bark, not the fruit, which is used to make the poison, and except for the new branches growing high among the trees from which the liana hangs, its twisted stems bear few leaves. Whether or not he came close to the solution of a problem that baffled succeeding generations, Oviedo immediately thereafter descended to the same lurid mixture of fantasy and speculation that seemed to bedevil most of the early writers about the New World. He wrote: "These trees for the most part grow ever by the sea coasts and near unto the water. And are so fair and pleasant that there is no man that seeth them but will desire to eat thereof. In so much that it may be spoken of any frute yet growing on the earth, I would say that this was the unhappy frute whereof our first parents Adam and Eve tasted, whereby both lost their felicity and procured death to them and their posterity. Of these frutes, and of the great ants whose biting causeth swelling . . . and vipers and such other venomous things, the cannibals which are the chief archers among the Indians are accustomed to poison their arrowes, wherewith they kill all that they wound. These venoms they mingle together and make thereof a black mass or composition which appeareth like unto very black pitch."

Oviedo had obviously seen curare, since the raw poison is a dark, sticky substance that does look like tar. But soon he is off among the fables again: "If a man do but repose himself to sleep a little while under the shadow of the tree, he hath his head and eyes so swollen when he riseth that the eyelids are joined with the cheeks. And if it chance one drop or more of the dewe of the said tree do fall into the eye, it utterly destroyeth the sight . . . The wood of these trees when it burneth maketh so great a stink that no man is able to abide it, by reason it causeth so great a pain in the head."

Early travelers, exposed to such a sinister poison, naturally sought an antidote to it. Oviedo wrote that "the Christians in those parts" believed that "there is no remedy so profitable . . . as is the water of the sea, if the wound be much washed therewith, by which means some have escaped, although but few." Even though no effective antidote to curare was discovered until modern times, faith in the healing properties of sea water, or salt, continued for many years. Paradoxically enough, sugar was also often mentioned as an antidote.

58

Tobacco, too, was advanced as the remedy by the first doctor to write about curare, Nicolas Monardes, of Seville. Monardes published in 1569 and 1571 two volumes of an encyclopedic work with the splendid title "Joyfull Newes Out Of The Newe Worlde, wherein is declared the rare and singular virtues of diverse and sundrie hearbes, trees, oils, plants and stones, with their applications, as well for physic as chirurgerie, the said being well applied bringeth such present remedy for all diseases as may seem altogether incredible; notwithstanding by practice found out to be true." Monardes was a great believer in tobacco, which had lately been imported to Europe from America. He wrote of its "marvellous medicinable virtues" and stated that its leaves, warmed in the embers of a fire and applied as a sort of poultice, would "heal griefs of the head and of the stomach, kidney stones, and griefs of the joints, swellings, tooth-ache and chilblains."

And this was not all. "One of the marvels of this hearbe," he said, "is the manner how the priests of the Indies did use of it. When there was amongst the Indians any manner of business of great importance . . . the chief priest . . . took certain leaves of the Tabaco and cast them into the fire, and did receive the smoke of them at his mouth and at his nose with a cane, and in taking of it he fell down upon the ground, as a dead man . . . and when the hearbe had done his work, he did revive and awake, and gave them their answers, according to the visions and illusions which he saw." Tobacco, said Monardes, took away the weariness of all who smoked it and they awoke "much the lustier." He would have had a hard time with the Food and Drug Administration.

As for tobacco's usefulness as an antidote to curare, he wrote: "In venom and venomous wounds our Tabaco hath great experience . . . When the wild people of the Indies, which eat manne's fleshe, do shoot their arrowes, they do anoint them with an hearbe or composition made of many poisons, . . . and this venom is so evil and pernicious that it killeth without remedy, and they that be hurt dieth with great pains and accidents, and with madness, unless they had found remedy for so great an evil." The remedy adopted by some Indians as well as Spaniards, said Monardes, was "to put upon the wounds the juice of the Tabaco, and the leaves [pounded to powder]. And God would, that putting it upon the hurts, the griefs, madness and

59

accidents wherewith they died was mitigated, and in such sort they were delivered of that evil."

Garlic was another antidote sometimes recommended, though it was not always clear whether it was supposed to be eaten or rubbed in the wound. One method must have been as futile as the other, but the efficacy of garlic was accepted by no less eminent a traveler than Sir Walter Raleigh. Soldier, sailor, poet, courtier, administrator, and man of action, Raleigh sent several expeditions to the Americas, including the one that founded the ill-fated English settlement on Roanoke Island, off the coast of North Carolina. In one of his periodic exiles from the court of the fickle Queen Elizabeth I, he resolved to go in search of the fabulous city of gold, El Dorado, the mythical paradise that lured so many adventurers to their deaths in the vast interior of South America.

The legend of El Dorado had its genesis in a custom of the Chibcha Indians of Colombia which had lapsed long before the white man arrived in the New World. Every year, the tribe's young chief was rubbed with oil and then rolled in gold dust, which he washed off with ceremonial rites in a lake. From a golden prince to a golden city was but a short leap for the imaginations of the conquistadors, who believed that El Dorado was so rich in treasure that the mountains surrounding it shone with gold.

As fast as one expedition failed to find the fabled city, its presumed location was shifted to somewhere else. Raleigh believed that Manoa, the lake on which it was supposed to stand, would be found on the Caroní, a tributary of the Orinoco, the great river that empties into the Atlantic in what is now Venezuela. He set out to find it in 1594, with five ships. He was unsuccessful, but he returned to England with his hopes undimmed and wrote a book containing many accurate observations of what he had seen, called *The Discovery of the Large Rich and Beautiful Empire of Guiana*. It was published in 1596, the same year in which his courage and fighting skill prevented the annihilation of a British expedition against the Spanish fortress of Cádiz.

Raleigh described several different tribes he had encountered on his travels, including one called the Aroras who, he said, were as black as Negroes but had straight hair; a "rather desperate people" who used a strong poison on their arrows. "There was nothing whereof I was more curious," he wrote, "than to find out the true remedies of these poisoned arrows, for besides the mortalitie of the wound they make, the partie shot endureth the most insufferable torment in the world, and abideth a most uglie and lamentable death, sometimes dying stark mad, sometimes their bowels breaking out of their bellies, and are presently discolored, as black as pitch, and so unsavory as no man can endure to cure, or to attend them." Since only a slight wound was usually inflicted by the Indians' blow darts or arrows, he must here have been describing wounds that had become seriously infected.

"And it is more strange to know that in all this time there was never Spaniard either by gift or torment that could attain to the true knowledge of the cure, although they have martyred and put to invented torture I know not how many of them. But every one of these Indians know it not, no not one among thousands, but their soothsayers and priests, who do conceal it, and only teach it but from the father to the son.

"These medicines which . . . serve for the ordinary poison are made of the juice of a root called *Tupara;* the same also quencheth marvellously the heat of burning fevers and healeth inward wounds and broken veins that bleed within the body . . . Some of the Spaniards have been cured in ordinary wounds of the common poisoned arrows with the juice of garlicke, but this is a general rule for all men that shall hereafter travel the Indies where poisoned arrows are used, that they must abstain from drink, for if they take any licor into their body, as they shall be marvellously provoked thereunto by drought . . . there is no way with them but present death."

The thirst alleged to follow wounds caused by poisoned arrows was mentioned by several later writers but, notwithstanding Raleigh's warning, if the arrow really bore curare it would make precious little difference to the victim whether his thirst was slaked with water or "licor" or not at all. A few years after his expedition, and despite his bravery at Cádiz, Raleigh fell victim to court intrigues and was sentenced to die on the execution block for treason. Imprisoned in the Tower of London, he set about writing a history of the world which he was never to finish. He was released from the Tower to make a second expedition to South America in 1617. He traveled a short way up the

Orinoco but was no more successful in finding El Dorado than he had been before—and this second expedition ended in disaster. His son, also called Walter, was killed in a battle with the Spaniards on the Caroní river, and even though he had been warned in London not to molest the Spaniards, Raleigh captured a Spanish town. This time, when he returned to London, he was executed.

One of Raleigh's lieutenants on both his expeditions was an adventurous scholar named Laurence Keymis, who committed suicide in despair after leading the foray up the Caroní river on which young Raleigh was killed. After he returned from his first journey, Keymis published a book about Guiana in which he listed names of rivers, trees, plants, and animals he had encountered in his travels. Under the heading "poisonous herbs" he set down the word *"ourari."* This was only one of an assortment of names by which the "flying death" was known until the term "curare" gained popular acceptance fairly recently. Also used were: *woorali, woorala, wourali, wourara, urari, uiraery, cururu, curuiri, curara,* and many others. These variations were probably all attempts to reproduce the Indian phrase *uiraery,* a compound of the words *uira,* a bird, and *eor,* to kill—though even this is not certain, since one authority suggested that the term comes from *ur,* to come, and *ar,* to fall. It may also have developed from *cura,* the word used for a blowpipe in parts of Guiana.

This confusion over what to call the poison was exceeded only by the confusion about its origin, which persisted for three centuries. The various lianas from which curare is made grow deep in the tangled jungles that clothe much of the millions of square miles drained by the two immense river systems of the northern half of South America, the Amazon and the Orinoco. The Amazon rises in the Andes, not much more than a hundred miles from the Pacific Ocean, and flows three thousand miles across the continent, fed by innumerable tributaries until it pours its mud-stained waters into the South Atlantic off the coast of northern Brazil. The Orinoco rises in southern Venezuela, about four hundred miles north of the Amazon, and flows first west, then north, and finally east to the Atlantic.

Parts of the vast area through which these great rivers and their tributaries flow are still mysterious and all but inaccessible today. The whole of it was closed to all but Spanish and Portu-

62

guese eyes by a treaty drawn up in the little Spanish wine-making town of Tordesillas in 1494. This treaty followed with some agreed modifications an extraordinary papal bull issued the year before by Pope Alexander VI dividing the non-Christian world between Spain and Portugal. Under it, Portugal was allotted sovereignty over part of what is now Brazil and all of Africa, and Spain was given all the "newe-founde lands" west of Brazil. The other nations of Europe protested against this arbitrary division of the spoils to be expected from colonization of the New World, but it lasted for many years. Pirates operating with the tacit approval of their kings might nibble at the edges of this empire and sack a port here and there, but the great interior of South America remained as remote to other European nations as the face of the moon. And since the Spaniards and Portuguese were more concerned with the material riches of their dominions and the souls of their inhabitants than with scientific inquiry, real knowledge was slow to replace the fantasies propagated by the early travelers.

The first foreign scientist to pierce this "papal curtain" was also to become the first man to take samples of curare back to Europe for investigation. Charles Marie de La Condamine, born in Paris in 1701, first heard of the wonders of South America from a Spanish prisoner when, as a boy of eighteen, he was serving as an officer in the French Army. The stories kindled his "ardent curiosity," which Voltaire was later to praise, and he took up the study of mathematics and the evolving science of geodesy, which was concerned with measuring the size and shape of the earth. At the age of twenty-nine, La Condamine was elected to the French Academy of Sciences and a few years later he was chosen to head an expedition to South America charged with resolving the dispute between adherents of the Englishman Isaac Newton, who said the earth was flattened at the poles and bulged outwards at the equator, and supporters of the Frenchman Jacques Cassini, who believed the opposite.

La Condamine's surveys and measurements had to be done at the equator and since equatorial Africa was still even more of a closed book than South America, King Philip V of Spain permitted the expedition to work out of Quito, the capital of Ecuador. It was the first foreign expedition with royal sanction for two and a half centuries and the king took the precaution of sending a couple of Spanish naval officers along to police it. Entering into the scientific spirit of things, these officers sent back a valuable series of observations on the territory in which they found themselves, but such was the Spanish desire to keep South America hidden from prying eyes that they were suppressed for years.

Quito, only a few miles from the equator, stands 9350 feet above sea level and is itself overshadowed by even higher, snow-covered volcanoes, including the mighty Chimborazo, which was thought to be the highest mountain in the world until the discovery of the Himalayas. La Condamine arrived in South America in 1735 and after a long overland journey to Quito spent six years shivering among those hostile peaks, clambering thousands of feet above the city to set out his triangulation marks and take his measurements. Long before his work was completed, a sister expedition sent to Lapland had confirmed the Newtonians' theories, but La Condamine continued to amass the store of information which would later fill several books. Eight years after his arrival in South America, his geodesical work was completed. But he spurned the easy route home and set off by canoe to become the first scientist to travel across the continent down the Amazon.

Altogether, La Condamine spent ten years in South America and when he returned to Paris it was with far more than the measurements he had set out to make. He had come across a tribe of Indians who had shown him how they cut grooves in a tree, collected the milky sap that oozed out and poured it into leaves to set. The resilient, stretchy "cloth" thus formed—the Indians called it *caoutchouc*—kept out water and La Condamine used some of it to fashion a pouch to keep his instruments dry. He also packed away some samples to take home—and thus became the first man to focus Europe's attention on rubber.

He found another tribe throwing roots into a river and with his "ardent curiosity" waited to see what happened. Soon, stunned fish began to float to the surface and the Indians scooped them up in wicker baskets. Some of these roots went into La Condamine's baggage, too, and he was able to introduce Europe to *barbasco,* which contains a poison called rotenone, now widely used as an insecticide. At yet another place he collected a grayish white ore—and became the first man to take platinum to

Europe. Day after day, as he was swept along, now bouncing through roaring rapids, now drifting on broad, sluggish stretches of the vast river, he measured its width, plumbed its depths, and drew remarkably accurate maps of its course.

And then, too, there was curare. The Amazon is formed by two other rivers rising in the Andes, the Marañón and the Ucayali. Near their junction, La Condamine encountered an Indian tribe called the Yameos, about whom he later wrote: "The *Yameos* propel by the breath small arrows of wood [blow darts], to a distance of thirty or forty paces, and rarely miss their target . . . They cover the points of these little arrows, as well as those used with the bow, with a poison so active that, when it is fresh, it will kill in less than a minute any animal whose blood it has entered. Although we had our fowling pieces, we hardly ate anything killed in any other way than by these darts . . . There is no danger from this; the poison only kills if it enters the blood; but it is no less mortal to man than to animals. The antidote is salt, but of safe dependence, sugar."

La Condamine was anxious to test the curare, and the effectiveness of the supposed antidotes, for himself. While waiting for the ship that was to carry him home from Cayenne, on the east coast of South America, he invited the governor of the colony, some officers of the garrison, and the king's physician to watch his demonstration. First, he wounded a chicken with a blow dart he had been given thirteen months before, already coated with the poison. The bird died in about seven minutes.* Next, he pricked another chicken with an arrow freshly dipped in one of the samples he planned to take back to France. Even though he immediately pulled out the arrow and forced sugar into the chick-

---

* Curare retains its virulence for many years. In 1889 the *British Medical Journal* described a case in which a twenty-three-year-old housemaid fell off a stepladder while dusting shields and other relics on the wall of an English stately home. As she fell, her arm was impaled by an arrow "thought to have been poisoned with *wourali*." Even though the arrow was pulled out almost immediately, the girl collapsed and eventually stopped breathing. The doctor had to "pass an interrupted galvanic current" through her diaphragm and give her artificial respiration for more than an hour before she revived. Also in England, just before World War II, Dr. Ranyard West carried out some important experiments in the treatment of tetanus with curare—using a sample of the poison collected from the jungle more than thirty years earlier.

en's beak, it too died. La Condamine again dipped the arrow in the poison and jabbed it into a third chicken. This one, surprisingly, "having had the same remedy immediately administered, exhibited no sign of the least inconvenience."

Back in Europe, La Condamine repeated his experiment for a group of eminent doctors at Leiden, in the Netherlands. He was unable to show that sugar had any value as an antidote—the bird to which he gave it lived only a little longer than the others—but his graphic demonstration of the power of the "flying death," which had hitherto been merely another lurid traveler's tale, prompted the first investigations of the poison in Europe. Some of the poison La Condamine took home had come from the Ticunas, a tribe living on the banks of the Marañón, and he reported that they used no fewer than thirty different roots and herbs to make it. The most important ingredients, he thought, were several varieties of creepers—a hunch that came close to the truth.

The next explorer to write about curare, an extraordinary and many-sided adventurer named Edward Bartholomew Bancroft, pointed out that the composition of the poison varied according to which tribe concocted it. But he recognized that the active ingredient came from lianas. Largely self-taught, Bancroft was a physician, a pioneer in applied chemistry, a zoologist, and one of the most successful double agents in the history of espionage. Born into an illustrious New England family at Westfield, Massachusetts, in 1744, he ran away to sea as a boy and might have received some medical training as a surgeon's mate, since while still in his teens he turned up as a medical attendant on a plantation in Surinam. His three years in South America furnished him with the material for a book about the people, animals, and plants of Guiana which he published in 1769, a few years after going to London to study medicine, at the age of twenty-one. The book established his reputation as a scientist and he later became the leading authority of his day on dyestuffs, which he had begun to study after seeing them used by the natives of Surinam.

Such were Bancroft's many talents that he soon became a fashionable physician—he lived for a time in Downing Street, later to become famous as the home of British prime ministers—and when he was proposed for membership in the Royal Society in 1773 his sponsors were the astronomer royal, the king's physician and Benjamin Franklin. Some time before the War of Independence broke out, Franklin enlisted Bancroft's services as a spy. But he immediately reported to the British government and began to ply the hazardous trade of double agent. In 1776 he informed the British about the secret negotiations between the colonists and France. Later, when the Americans began to doubt his loyalty, he had himself arrested by the British for complicity in a plot to blow up dockyards. "Exiled" to Paris, he was made secretary to the American Commission by Franklin. He continued to supply information to the British, though he held up news of Burgoyne's surrender at Saratoga long enough to make a killing on the London Stock Exchange. His services were evidently appreciated, since in 1780 his salary as a British agent was doubled from £500 to £1000.

Bancroft retained the loyalty and friendship of both Americans and British and died in 1821, at the age of seventy-seven, universally respected and admired. His career as a spy did not come to light until seventy years after his death, and when it did his grandson, a British general, was so upset that he destroyed most of Bancroft's papers and correspondence.

Not the least remarkable of Bancroft's achievements was to ferret out a recipe for curare while he was working in Surinam and was not yet twenty-one. He said he received it from the *peiis,* or witch doctors, and he was the first white man to describe the preparation of curare in any detail. Mentioning La Condamine's statement that thirty constituents went into the Ticunas' poison, he contrasted that with the curare made by the Accawaus, which contained only five, "though the other nations, particularly the *Arrowauks,* make several whimsical additions, among which are the teeth and livers of venomous snakes and red pepper." Bancroft said the Accawau poison-makers who had told him their secrets all agreed on the number and identity of the ingredients, "but with some variation in their quantities which, indeed, they have no method of either expressing or ascertaining with exactness." The recipe was: "Take of the Bark of the Root of *Woorara,* six parts; Of the Bark of *Warracobba coura,* two parts; Of the Bark of the Roots of *Couranapi, Baketi* and *Hatchybaly,* of each one part."

These ingredients, said Bancroft, should be scraped and simmered in a pot for a quarter of an hour, after which the juice should be squeezed out with the hands, "taking care that the skin is unbroken"—an eminently reasonable precaution. The juice should then be evaporated over a fire until it had the consistency of tar, whereupon it should be smeared on pieces of wood and stored in a hollow cane, closed at both ends with skins. The poison would solidify as it cooled, but it could be softened when needed by either dissolving it in water or holding the pieces of wood over a fire until the curare melted and became soft again.

It was a good description, but because of the mystery surrounding the poison's preparation, Bancroft did not actually see it made. The first European to do that was Friedrich Heinrich Alexander, Baron von Humboldt, the universal genius who rivaled Napoleon in fame and outshone every other man of his age in the breadth and scale of his scientific accomplishments. Son of a wealthy Prussian army officer and a French mother, von Humboldt studied geology, among other things, and by the time he was twenty-three had been appointed director general of mines in Franconia. But no single scientific discipline could contain his restless, towering intellect. He made the whole world his field of study and contributed pioneer researches in a dozen sciences ranging from astronomy to zoology.

In 1799 von Humboldt arrived in South America with a man who was to be his lifelong friend and collaborator, Aimé Bonpland, a surgeon who preferred the roving life of a plant collector to the confines of the operating room. During the next four years they traveled forty thousand miles exploring the frigid mountain peaks and humid jungles of what are now Peru, Ecuador, Colombia, and Venezuela. Bonpland returned to Europe with sixty thousand plants, including more than three thousand new species. Von Humboldt studied everything from the magnetism of the earth to the fertilizing properties of bird droppings, or guano; from the Aztec calendar to the electric eel; from ocean currents to the effect of curare on the nerves of the frog.

Arriving at Quito, where La Condamine had made his measurements sixty-five years before, von Humboldt studied the effect of altitude on climate and zones of vegetation. He had already found out that as he worked northward from the equator the mean temperature dropped one degree with each degree of latitude; now he discovered that the same drop in temperature occurred with each three hundred feet climbed up a mountain. With Bonpland, he set out to scale the twenty-two-thousand-foot Mount Chimborazo. They edged along icy ridges only inches wide and reached an altitude of more than nineteen thousand feet before an impossible crevasse halted their progress. It was higher than man had ever climbed before, so high that their eyes and gums began to bleed—and von Humboldt discovered the perils of oxygen starvation.

Then they descended to Quito, mounted their horses and set off on a thousand-mile exploration of the Andes to the south. Von Humboldt studied Inca ruins and became the first writer on the ancient archeology of South America. He journeyed on the Amazon and corrected La Condamine's charts. He poked into ancient mines and questioned people everywhere he went about the past, so that later he became the first writer to give Europe a hint of the lost cultures of the Aztecs, Incas, and Mayans.

After his return to Europe, von Humboldt was to write twenty-nine books on South America, illustrated by hundreds of his own sketches and maps. In one of these, his *Personal Narrative,* he described how he had seen curare made at a settlement called Esmeralda, on the banks of the Orinoco near its source in southern Venezuela. When the explorers arrived at Esmeralda they found its people returning from an expedition into the jungle to collect the lianas needed to make the poison. They were celebrating their return with a festival, and as at similar celebrations in other places and at other times, the wine of the country was flowing freely. Von Humboldt wrote:

We were fortunate enough to find an old Indian less drunk than the others, who was employed in preparing curare poison from the freshly-gathered plants. He was the chemist of the place. We found at his hut large earthen pots for boiling the vegetable juice, shallower vessels offering a favorable surface for evaporation, and leaves of the plantain tree rolled up in the shape of our filters, and used to filtrate the liquids which are more or less loaded with fibrous material. He insisted upon the greatest order and neatness in his hut, which was transformed into a chemical laboratory. The Indian who instructed us is known throughout the mission by the name of the poison-master (*amo del curare*). He had that self-sufficient air and tone of pedantry of which the pharmacopolists of Europe were formerly accused.

"I know," he said, "that the whites have the secret of making soap, and manufacturing the black powder that has the defect of making a loud noise when used in killing animals. The curare, the secret of whose preparation is handed down from father to son, is superior to anything you make *down yonder* (beyond the sea). It is the juice of an herb that kills silently, without anyone knowing from whence the stroke comes."

Von Humboldt watched the old Indian scrape the bark from the lianas he had previously collected and pound it into fibers on a flat stone. "The venomous juice is yellow," he wrote, "and the whole fibrous mass takes on the same color. It is thrown into a funnel nine inches high, with an opening four inches wide. This funnel was, of all the instruments in the Indian laboratory, the one of which the poison-master was most proud. He asked us repeatedly if *por alla* (out yonder, meaning Europe), we had seen anything to be compared with his funnel (*embudo*). It was the leaf of a plantain tree rolled up in the form of a cone, and placed within another stronger cone made of the leaves of the palm tree."

Having placed the funnel into an earthen pot, the old Indian then began to pour water on the crushed bark fibers, a tedious procedure he kept up for several hours, during which a yellowish liquid slowly dripped into the pot. "This filtered water is the poisonous liquor," von Humboldt wrote, "but it acquires strength only when concentrated by evaporation, as molasses." From time to time during the long boiling process, the old man invited his visitor to taste the liquid, explaining that its bitterness indicated the degree of its concentration. "There is no danger in tasting it," said von Humboldt, "the curare being dangerous only when it comes in immediate contact with the blood stream."

He added that no amount of concentration made the liquid thick enough to coat the Indian's blow darts, so to give it body he laced it with the sticky juice of a tree called kiracagnero. "At the instant when the glutinous juice of the kiracagnero tree is poured into the venomous liquor well concentrated, and kept in a state of ebullition, it turns black and coagulates into a mass of the consistency of tar, or of a thick syrup. This mass is the curare of commerce. The curare is sold in little calabashes, but its preparation being in the hands of a few families, and the quantity of poison attached to each dart being extremely small, the best curare, that of Esmeralda and Mandavaca, is sold at a very high price."

Von Humboldt went on to mention several other kinds of curare, including La Condamine's Ticunas "which have been too vaguely linked together under the name of 'American arrow poisons'" and said they were not all made from the same species of plant. He also made the accurate prediction that some day the alkaloid, or active principle, of the poison would be isolated from the plants as the drug morphine had been isolated from opium.

One morning on his way home from Esmeralda, von Humboldt was about to put on his socks when something prompted him to feel inside them. They were wet and when he looked into his baggage to discover why, he found that a bottle containing some of the poison he had collected had spilled among his clothes. His feet were bleeding badly at the time from the bites of insects called *chegoes*. Had he pulled on those socks, the "flying death" would have claimed its most eminent victim, and the world would have been denied the fruits of the masterly scientific investigations von Humboldt continued to make almost until his death in 1859, at the age of ninety.

chapter

6

Even before von Humboldt set out for South America, European investigators had begun to experiment with curare. In 1747, two years after La Condamine poisoned his chickens at Leiden, the work was taken up by an English physician named Richard Brocklesby, a fashionable London doctor who went to school with Edmund Burke and attended Dr. Johnson in his last illness. Brocklesby cut open a cat's nose and smeared curare given him by La Condamine into the wound. "In half an hour," he wrote to the president of the Royal Society, the cat "seemed, by mewing more than before, to be sensible of some pain. Thus she remained about twenty minutes, when at length she shivered, was sleepy, soon became convulsed and in about half an hour her limbs were flaccid and her belly swell'd. These symptoms continued till she in a short time expired." When the cat seemed to be dead, Brocklesby cut off its head and examined its brain. He found no injury, no abnormality, nothing to explain the cat's death. Then he opened its chest, and to his astonishment saw that its heart was still beating, "as if the animal were in perfect health."

The fact that the cat went into convulsions suggests that the curare was not pure, that its jungle maker had hedged his bets by adulterating it with such other poisons as snake venom or ant stings. This was a problem that bedeviled all investigators until modern times. But Brocklesby, right at the start of the investigations, had established an important fact—that the poison had no action on the heart. However, he was a careful man. Perhaps the cat had not really been dead? Certainly other scientists who might examine his conclusions could say that. So he repeated the experiment with a dog. It promptly became sleepy and "so stupid that he suffered himself to be often burned by the hot ashes beneath the grate, where he lay for warmth." Brocklesby seems not to have suspected that paralysis, rather than stupidity, might have accounted for the dog's lethargy. Next morning, having found it back to normal, he injected more curare into one of its veins, and this time it died. There was no doubt about it, the dog was dead. But once again, there was still a heartbeat for some time after death. Now Brocklesby killed two birds with the poison, having given them sugar and found it "no manner of use." He fed the two birds to two cats which, "whether from eating them or not I don't pretend to say . . . made so uncommon a noise the whole night that they disturbed the family's rest."

Brocklesby's chief finding—that the poison did not affect the heart—was essentially a negative one. But many later investigators were to have no more luck in fathoming curare's mysteries. The next experiments were performed a year later by a French doctor named Hérissant, who obviously had a healthy respect for curare and imagined he had proved the truth of the legend that its fumes were fatal to its makers—a story La Condamine also believed.

Hérissant began his work in 1748 by evaporating the curare in a small closet in which "a young lad was at work." Leaving the poison bubbling on the heat to reach the right consistency, Hérissant busied himself in the next room until he suddenly noticed that the young lad seemed to be loafing, as young lads sometimes do.

"I began to reprimand him for his laziness," the good doctor wrote, "but he excused himself by answering, with a trembling voice, that he was sick at heart, and felt himself very faint. 'Tis easy to imagine the uneasiness which this sight gave me;

but luckily it cost me no more than the fright. I made the lad come out of the closet immediately, led him down to the yard and made him swallow a pint of good wine, in which I had dissolved a quartern of sugar. He recovered his strength by degrees and was soon able to return to his own home, very merry and happy, without the least notion of the danger he had been in." The danger, if indeed there had been any, must have come from the building up of carbon monoxide fumes in the enclosed space, rather than the curare. But Hérissant pressed on intrepidly. "The fact above related," he wrote, "was shocking enough to make me abandon my project; however, curiosity got the better of my fear."

So next day, he himself supervised the boiling down of the extract. Sure enough, within an hour, "I perceived my legs to bend under me and my arms became so weak that I could scarcely use them." Retiring from the closet in some haste and, as he thought, in the nick of time, Hérissant administered to himself the remedy that had made his young lad so merry, and thus restored went back to work. But this was not the end of his misadventures. Having concentrated the curare, he stoppered it up tightly in a glass phial. Curare can ferment under certain conditions and when Hérissant picked up the phial some days later "the cork flew up to the ceiling with vast rapidity" and some of the poison splashed out. It was a hot day and he was working stripped to the waist. "I was so stupefied at this un-expected accident that I imagined (as it was very possible) that the bottle was broken in pieces, and as soon as I saw my hands, arms and breast colored in several places by the poison, which had besprinkled them in the explosion, I looked on myself as a dead man; which must certainly have been the case if the bottle had burst and the pieces of glass had cut me."

Fortunately the phial was intact—and surprisingly enough so was Hérissant's patience, for he went on to administer the poison to dozens of animals, including rabbits, wolves, horses, a bear, and an eagle. All were affected by the poison in varying degrees, though he could not get the same results in fish and reptiles. Hérissant's chief conclusions were that an animal poisoned by curare does not feel pain; that it suffers a "sudden and almost universal palsy"; and that neither sugar nor sea salt could be considered an antidote.

The next investigator to turn his attention to "the American poison" was the Abbé Felice Fontana, a renowned physiologist and anatomist. Less given to dramatics than Hérissant, and more thorough, Fontana carried out an important series of experiments in Florence in 1780. First, by holding a pigeon's head in the pot containing his curare, and then by making it breathe the vapor given off as the poison was burned on hot coals, he concluded that its fumes, despite the legends, were "perfectly innocent." Then he fed the poison to pigeons and guinea pigs and concluded that though it could be fatal when taken by mouth "it takes a pretty large quantity of it to kill even a small animal."

Much more impressive was the result when he injected the poison into a rabbit's jugular vein. It "fell down as dead as if it had been struck by lightning." Fontana had spent two years investigating the effects of viper venom. Curare, he reported, when introduced directly into the blood, killed faster than the snake poison. After dozens of experiments on various animals, he decided that curare's action was "all upon the blood," and that though it did not affect the action of the heart, it destroyed the ability of muscles to react to impulses from the nerves. He was not quite correct in this conclusion, but it was to be many more years before anyone came closer to understanding the poison's true action.

It is impossible not to admire the perseverance and to sympathize with the frustrations of the early seekers after curare's elusive secrets. Exactly how it produces its strange, wilting type of paralysis was still a matter for speculation and neurological research until recent times. In the eighteenth and nineteenth centuries, when so much less was known about the mechanism of the body, trying to understand curare's action was like trying to discover bacteria without access to a microscope. Then, too, right up until World War II an investigator could not be sure of getting the same results from two different batches of the poison, since their strength and composition varied so much and the true curare effect was quite likely to be masked or modified by the presence of snake venom or some other unsuspected impurity. The perfectly reasonable conclusions of one experimenter might thus be contradicted by another, equally reasonable. As for foreseeing curare's eventual role in anesthesia, how could the most perspicacious genius do that when anesthesia itself had still to be discovered?

And yet the wonder is that the most important lesson of all about the "flying death," the lesson that was to give Harold Griffith the confidence to introduce it into the operating room, was learned more than thirty years before William Morton showed how ether could blot out the pain of surgery. This lesson, which the world was so unaccountably slow to grasp, was simply that if an animal paralyzed by curare was kept alive by artificial respiration, the effect of the poison would eventually wear off. For the successful demonstration of this vital fact we are indebted to the unlikely collaboration of a scholarly young doctor who later became one of the most distinguished surgeons of his day; a resolutely amateur bird collector and taxidermist who was one of the most engaging characters in the whole rich gallery of English eccentrics; and a donkey.

Benjamin Collins Brodie was born in Wiltshire in 1783 and was educated by his father until he took up medicine at the age of eighteen. He studied under the leading London surgeons and progressed rapidly in his profession, being elected a Fellow of the Royal Society at the age of twenty-seven. In 1819 he was appointed professor of comparative anatomy and physiology of the Royal College of Surgeons, and in this capacity he assisted at an operation to remove a tumor from the royal scalp of King George IV—an operation after which the surgeons spent many sleepless nights until it was clear that the king would not succumb to the almost universal infection that still followed even minor surgery. In his later years Brodie became president of the Royal Society, president of the Royal College of Surgeons, and a member of several august international scientific societies.

When still a young man, he studied the effects on the system of several different vegetable poisons, including strychnine and the notorious sap of the Upas tree of Southeast Asia, as well as curare. Experimenting on guinea pigs with "woorara," he confirmed that the heart continued to beat after the animals' chests had become paralyzed and they had stopped breathing. This led him to wonder what would happen if he kept them breathing by artificial respiration after they were apparently dead. He paralyzed a cat with curare and after she appeared to have died cut a hole in her windpipe, or trachea—he was one of the first to perform this operation, called a tracheotomy, which is sometimes used in emergencies to save patients from suffocation. Brodie put a tube into the opening he had made and forced air into the cat's lungs with a pair of bellows. After forty minutes, he saw that her pupils were beginning to react to changes in the level of light, but she remained motionless. An hour later, she began to twitch and seemed to be trying to breathe for herself. After a further hour, her efforts succeeded, she began to breathe, and Brodie was able to give up his pumping of the bellows. He wrote later: "She lay, as if in a state of profound sleep, for forty minutes, when she suddenly awoke and walked away."

Brodie published the results of his experiments in the Philosophical Transactions of the Royal Society in 1811 and 1812. He was to reach a much wider audience with the arrival on the scene a couple of years later of the wildly improbable Charles Waterton, Squire of Walton Hall, and his donkey. Explorer, naturalist, writer, and utter individualist, Waterton feared neither man nor beast. He once captured a ten-foot boa constrictor by seizing its tail in his left hand and, when the snake raised its head to protest at this indignity, stunning it with a right to the head. As a young man, even though he was a devout Roman Catholic, he scaled the outside of St. Peter's church in Rome and left his gloves on the tip of the lightning conductor surmounting the cross on its dome. To the end of his days—he lived to the spry old age of eighty-two—he delighted in kicking off his shoes and scrambling up a tree to inspect a bird's nest or merely to perch among its branches reading his favorite Latin poets. At the age of forty-eight, he married a girl of seventeen, the orphaned daughter of an old friend, and after she died in childbirth less than a year later he never again slept in a bed: he would curl up on the floor in a blanket or old coat, a wooden block for his pillow.

Charles Waterton was born in 1782 into a Yorkshire family that traced its ancestry back to before the Norman conquest of England. He went to school at Stonyhurst, a Roman Catholic college in Lancashire, where the priests, recognizing his predilection for wild life, made him "official rat-catcher." He learned little there about natural science, or indeed any other science, but did pick up the habit of peppering long Latin quotations through his writings and—if we accept the accuracy of the passages of high-flown dialogue sprinkled through his books—his speech.

At the age of twenty-two, Waterton set out to manage three plantations owned by his family in Demerara (which later became British Guiana and received independence as Guyana, in 1966). Growing coffee and cotton and supervising the labors of a thousand black slaves soon proved far too tedious for the Squire's adventurous tastes and he took to splashing through the swamps beyond the plantation in search of the gaudy birds that inhabited them. The recurrent attacks of malaria brought on by these forays he shook off with a rugged constitution that remained unimpaired until his death, bolstered by liberal doses of quinine and other medicines, including jalap, in which he was a great believer. He also carried a lancet on his expeditions and if overtaken by fever would open a vein and draw off some of his own blood—he called it "tapping the claret." He bled himself well over a hundred times during his lifetime and his family doctor wrote that even in his eightieth year he thought nothing of drawing off twenty-four ounces of his own blood.

Some time after the Squire started collecting his birds he devised a unique method of preserving them which was a great improvement on the practice of contemporary taxidermists. He soaked the skins in corrosive sublimate, or mercuric chloride, which not only prevented them from decaying but kept them flexible for several days, during which Waterton would mold them into their natural shapes. When the skins dried they hardened into lifelike representations of the living creatures without benefit of internal supports or stuffing. So skillful did Waterton become in this plastic art that he was able to fashion grotesque creations combining parts of different animals and birds. These took their place in the private museum he assembled in his ancestral home, Walton Hall, duly labeled with the names of individuals or institutions that had aroused his anger. He once imparted human features to the face of a howling monkey, scandalizing his Yorkshire neighbors, who suspected he had killed and mounted a human specimen.

In 1812 the Squire decided to venture further afield in search of specimens and handed over his plantations to relatives. By now he had also come across curare, which the people of the Demerara coast secured by barter from tribes in the interior, and

78

wanted to investigate its mysteries for himself. With a small party of Indians, he set off on the first of a series of remarkable journeys through the largely unexplored jungles of Guiana which he described in a book called *Wanderings in South America*. Published in 1825, this was immensely popular in nineteenth-century England, and indeed it is still in print, though some of its more florid passages and its many earnest asides to "you, gentle reader" have a quaint sound today. Waterton had little scientific training himself and was loftily scornful of those who had—he dismissed them as "closet naturalists"—and even though he filled his book with his beloved Latin quotations he consistently refused to use the Latin scientific names for birds and animals, preferring the local terms. This restricted the book's value and infuriated his more conventional scientific colleagues, but he was nevertheless an enthusiastic and accurate observer of nature and he gave the first trustworthy accounts of, among other things, the three-toed sloth and the weapons on which curare was used.

On his first journey, Waterton, who was then thirty, traveled about a thousand miles by canoe and on foot in four months. Whether in or out of the jungle, he had no use for the customary dress of the English gentleman. Once, calling on a neighbor in Yorkshire, he was to his delight sent round to the servants' entrance by a new butler who did not recognize him. Slogging through the rain forests of Guiana, he wore a shirt and trousers and that was about all. He seldom bothered with boots and socks, since "in dry weather they would have irritated the feet and retarded me in the chase of wild beasts; and in the rainy season they would have kept me in a perpetual state of damp and moisture."

From Stabroek (now Georgetown) the barefoot wanderer paddled up the Demerara river until he was halted by a waterfall. He had his canoe portaged for several days across country to the Essequibo river, which empties into the Atlantic between the mouths of the Amazon and the Orinoco, then continued on up the Essequibo and entered one of its tributaries, which he called the Apourapoura. Several more days' paddling brought him into the territory of a people well known for the potency of their curare, the Macusis—though the Squire, with his usual perversity, calls them Macoushis.

On the way he saw many examples of "a vine called the

bush-rope," which may well have been a curare-producing liana, though he could not have known that at the time. "Sometimes," he wrote, "you see it nearly as thick as a man's body, twisted like a corkscrew round the tallest trees and rearing its head high above their tops. At other times three or four of them, like strands in a cable, join tree and tree and branch and branch together. Others, descending from on high, take root as soon as their extremity touches the ground, and appear like shrouds and stays supporting the mainmast of a line-of-battle ship . . . Oftentimes a tree, above a hundred feet high, uprooted by the whirlwind, is stopped in its fall by these amazing cables of nature."

He also paused awhile to give the gentle reader an opportunity to consider the sloth. "His looks, his gestures and his cries all conspire to entreat you to take pity on him. These are the only weapons of defence which nature hath given him . . . Do not then level your gun at him or pierce him with a poisoned arrow—he has never hurt one living creature. A few leaves, and those of the commonest and coarsest kind, are all he asks for his support."

Here and there along the way, the Squire stopped to pick up "wourali" from the Indian "habitations" he passed through. He bought his first sample from an Indian who "said he had killed a number of wild hogs with it, and two tapirs." Taking nothing for granted, Waterton tried it out on "a middle-sized dog." His account of the experiment shows what an emotional gulf separated him from the more detached investigators who were slaughtering guinea pigs and rabbits with the poison back in Europe: "He was wounded in the thigh, in order that there might be no possibility of touching a vital part. In three or four minutes he began to be affected, smelt at every little thing on the ground around him, and looked wistfully at the wounded part. Soon after this he staggered, laid himself down, and never rose more. He barked once, though not as if in pain. His voice was low and weak; and in a second attempt it quite failed him . . . In a quarter of an hour after he had received the poison he was quite motionless . . . It makes a pitying heart ache to see a poor creature in distress and pain; and too often has the compassionate traveller occasion to heave a sigh as he journeys on. However, here, though the kind-hearted will be sorry to read of an unoffending animal doomed to death in order to satisfy a doubt, still it will be a relief to know that the victim was not tortured. The *wourali* poison destroys life's action so gently that the victim appears to be in no pain whatever; and probably, were the truth known, it feels none, saving the momentary smart at the time the arrow enters."

Later, the Squire chronicled the death throes of another "poor creature" killed by *wourali*, this time his old friend the three-toed sloth, or *ai*, as it is called locally. He wrote: "The *ai* was wounded in the leg, and put down on the floor about two feet from the table; it contrived to reach the leg of the table, and fastened itself on it, as if wishful to ascend. But this was its last advancing step." One by one, the sloth's legs lost their grip on the table leg and it sank to the ground, but so gently that no one would have suspected it was dying. "From the time the poison began to operate," he wrote, "you would have conjectured that sleep was overpowering it, and you would have exclaimed: *'Pressitque jacentem, dulcis et alta quies, placidaeque simillima morti.'*" Exclamations like that are not heard in the jungle every day, and one imagines Squire Waterton must have been a continual inspiration to his Indian companions.

Before submitting his "concise, unadorned" account of the preparation of *wourali* to his gentle reader, he suggested as though apologizing for it that "it may be of service to thee some time or other shouldst thou ever travel through the wilds where it is used." He need not have apologized, as his account shows:

A day or two before the Macoushi Indian prepares his poison he goes into the forest in quest of the ingredients. A vine grows in these wilds which is called *wourali*. It is from this that the poison takes its name, and it is the principal ingredient. When he has procured enough of this he digs up a root of a very bitter taste, ties them together, and then looks about for two kinds of bulbous plants which contain a green and glutinous juice. He fills a little quake which he carries on his back with the stalks of these; and lastly ranges up and down until he finds two species of ants. One of them is very large and black, and so venomous that its sting produces a fever; it is most commonly to be met with on the ground. The other is a little red ant which stings like a nettle, and generally has its nest under the leaf of a shrub. After obtaining these he has no more need to range the forest.

A quantity of the strongest Indian pepper is used, but this he has already planted round his hut. The pounded fangs of the *labarri* snake [probably the *fer-de-lance*] and those of the *counacouchi* [the bushmaster] are likewise added. These he commonly has in store, for when he kills a snake he generally extracts the fangs and keeps them by him.

Having thus found the necessary ingredients, he scrapes the *wourali* vine and bitter root into thin shavings and puts them into a kind of colander made of leaves. This he holds over an earthen pot, and pours water on the shavings: the liquor which comes through has the appearance of coffee. When a sufficient quantity has been procured the shavings are thrown aside. He then bruises the bulbous stalks and squeezes a proportionate quantity of their juice through his hands into the pot. Lastly the snakes' fangs, ants and pepper are bruised and thrown into it. It is then placed on a slow fire, and as it boils more of the juice of the *wourali* is added, according as it may be found necessary, and the scum is taken off with a leaf: it remains on the fire till reduced to a thick syrup of a deep brown colour. As soon as it has arrived at this state a few arrows are poisoned with it, to try its strength. If it answer the expectations it is poured out into a calabash, or little pot of Indian manufacture, which is carefully covered with a couple of leaves, and over them a piece of deer's skin tied round with a cord. They keep it in the most dry part of the hut, and from time to time suspend it over the fire to counteract the effects of dampness.

The act of preparing this poison is not considered as a common one: the savage may shape his bow, fasten the barb on the point of his arrow and make his other implements of destruction either lying in his hammock or in the midst of his family; but if he has to prepare the *wourali* poison, many precautions are supposed to be necessary.

The women and young girls are not allowed to be present, lest the *Yabahou,* or evil spirit, should do them harm. The shed under which it has been boiled is pronounced polluted, and abandoned ever after. He who makes the poison must eat nothing that morning, and must continue fasting as long as the operation lasts.

Waterton's observation about the women and girls was borne out by many later travelers. Some tribal traditions went even further and barred the poison-makers from sexual relations with women for several days before they retired into the jungle to boil the curare—not to safeguard the women but because it was believed that the poison was "a man thing," and contact with females would detract from its strength. In a similar way, the Jivaros of Ecuador forbid sexual intercourse or even the sight of women for some days before the ceremony of shrinking the heads of their captured enemies.

Describing the Macusis' weapons, the Squire wrote:

When a native of Macoushia goes in quest of feathered game or other birds he seldom carries his bow and arrows. It is the blow-pipe he then uses. This extraordinary tube of death is, perhaps, one of the greatest natural curiosities of Guiana. It is not found in the country of the Macoushi. Those Indians tell you that it grows to the south-west of them, in the wilds which extend betwixt them and the Río Negro. The reed must grow to an amazing length, as the part the Indians use is from ten to eleven feet long, and no tapering can be perceived in it, one end being as thick as the other. It is of a bright yellow colour, perfectly smooth both inside and out. It grows hollow, nor is there the least appearance of a knot or joint throughout the whole extent. The natives call it *ourah*. This of itself is too slender to answer the end of a blow-pipe, but there is a species of palma, larger and stronger, and common in Guiana, and this the Indians make use of as a case in which they put the *ourah*. It is brown, susceptible of a fine polish, and appears as if it had joints five or six inches from each other. It is called *samourah,* and the pulp inside is easily extracted by steeping it for a few days in water. Thus the *ourah* and the *samourah,* one within the other, form the blow-pipe of Guiana . . .

The arrow is from nine to ten inches long. It is made

out of the leaf of a species of palm tree called *coucourite*, hard and brittle, and pointed as sharp as a needle. About an inch of the pointed end is poisoned. The other end is burnt to make it still harder, and wild cotton is put round it for about an inch and a half. It requires considerable practice to put on this cotton well. It must just be large enough to fit the hollow of the tube and taper off to nothing downwards. They tie it on with a thread of silk-grass to prevent its slipping off the arrow . . .

With a quiver of poisoned arrows slung over his shoulder and with his blow-pipe in his hand, in the same position as a soldier carries his musket, see the Macoushi Indian advancing towards the forest in quest of *powises, maroudis, waracabas* and other feathered game.

These generally sit high up in the tall and tufted trees but still are not out of the Indian's reach, for his blow-pipe, at its greatest elevation, will send an arrow three hundred feet. Silent as midnight he steals under them, and so cautiously does he tread the ground that the fallen leaves rustle not beneath his feet. His ears are open to the least sound, while his eye, keen as that of the lynx, is employed in finding out the game in the thickest shade. Often he imitates their cry, and decoys them from tree to tree, till they are within range of his tube. Then taking a poisoned arrow from his quiver, he puts it in the blow-pipe and collects his breath for the fatal puff.

About two feet from the end through which he blows there are fastened two teeth of the *acouri,* and these serve him for a sight. Silent and swift the arrow flies, and seldom fails to pierce the object at which it is sent. Sometimes the wounded bird remains in the same tree where it was shot, and in three minutes falls down at the Indian's feet. Should he take wing his flight is of short duration, and the Indian, following the direction he has gone, is sure to find him dead.

If he is hunting bigger game such as peccari or deer, Waterton continues, the Macusi uses a bow six to seven feet long, with silk-grass cord, and arrows four or five feet long made from a yellow reed. "A piece of hard wood about nine inches long is inserted into the end of the reed, and fastened with cotton well waxed. A square hole an inch deep is then made in the end of this piece of hard wood, done tight round with cotton to keep it from splitting. Into this square hole is fitted a spike of *coucourite*-wood, poisoned, and which may be kept there or taken out at pleasure. A joint of bamboo, about as thick as your finger, is fitted on over the poisoned spike to prevent accidents."

To ensure that there is enough poison to kill these larger animals, the spikes receive three or four coats of it, being dried in the sun or over a fire between each one. "It is rather a tedious operation to make one of these arrows complete and as the Indian is not famed for industry, except when pressed by hunger, he has hit upon a plan of preserving his arrows which deserves notice. About a quarter of an inch above the part where the *coucourite* spike is fixed into the square hole he cuts it half through, and thus, when it has entered the animal, the weight of the arrow causes it to break off there, by which means the arrow falls to the ground uninjured, so that, should this be the only arrow he happens to have with him and should another shot immediately occur, he has only to take another poisoned spike out of his little bamboo box, fit it on its arrow and send it to its destination."

Waterton was astute enough to realize that the Indians had no antidote to the poison. (Recalling Raleigh's words, one wonders how many of them were tortured to death by the Spaniards for a "secret" they could not possibly have disclosed.) One passage in the Squire's discussion of alleged antidotes betrays his clownish sense of fun, which he never lost. "Had the Indians a sure antidote," he wrote, "it is likely they would carry it about with them or resort to it immediately after being wounded . . . and their confidence in its efficacy would greatly diminish the horror they betray when you point a poisoned arrow at them."

As further evidence to back up his conclusion that no antidote existed, he offered an "affecting story" told to him by an Indian who had lost a friend on a hunting trip four years earlier: "His companion took a poisoned arrow and sent it at a red monkey in a tree above him. It was nearly a perpendicular shot. The arrow missed the monkey, and in the descent struck him in the arm a little above the elbow. He was convinced it was all over with him. 'I shall never,' said he to his companion,

85

in a faltering voice, and looking at his bow as he said it, 'I shall never,' said he, 'bend this bow again.' And having said that, he took off his little bamboo poison-box, which hung across his shoulder, and putting it together with his bow and arrows on the ground, he laid himself down close by them, bid his companion farewell, and never spoke more."

After suffering several bouts of fever on this first journey, Waterton returned home to England with a "severe tertian ague" [malaria] which kept reminding him that his shattered frame, "starting and shivering in the inconstant blast, meagre and pale, the ghost of what it was," required repairs. It was three years before he fully recovered from the recurrent attacks of malaria, and it was during this period, in 1814, that he presided over the celebrated demonstration with the donkey that set the seal on Brodie's important discovery that artificial respiration would keep a curarized animal alive. As Waterton described it:

A she-ass received the *wourali* poison in the shoulder, and died apparently in ten minutes. An incision was then made in its windpipe and through it the lungs were regularly inflated for two hours with a pair of bellows. Suspended animation returned. The ass held up her head and looked around, but the inflating being discontinued she sank once more in apparent death. The artificial breathing was immediately recommenced, and continued without intermission for two hours more. This saved the ass from final dissolution: she rose up and walked about; she seemed neither in agitation or in pain. The wound through which the poison entered was healed without difficulty. Her constitution, however, was so severely affected that it was long a doubt if ever she would be well again. She looked lean and sickly for above a year, but began to mend the spring after, and by midsummer became fat and frisky.

The kind-hearted reader will rejoice on learning that Earl Percy, pitying her misfortunes, sent her down from London to Walton Hall, near Wakefield. There she goes by the name of *Wouralia*. Wouralia shall be sheltered from the wintry storm; and when summer comes she shall feed in the finest pasture. No burden shall be placed upon her, and she shall end her days in peace.

Why Wouralia should have been "lean and sickly" after this demonstration is a mystery, but the "kind-hearted reader" can rejoice again, for she suffered no lasting ill effects: she survived the operation by twenty-five years.

Presumably because of his distrust of orthodox scientists, Waterton did not mention that Brodie performed the tracheotomy on Wouralia, assisted by Professor William Sewell, president of the London Veterinary College. If this detracts somewhat from the Squire's contribution to the taming of the "flying death," at least it was he who initiated the demonstration—and he with his poisoned arrows who inflicted Wouralia's historic wound.

Ludicrous though some of Waterton's escapades and attitudes may have been, he has one quite genuine claim to fame. His love of birds led him to devise all sorts of imaginative nesting places for them in the trees and buildings around his Yorkshire home. He liked poachers no more than "closet naturalists" and so to keep them out he eventually built a three-mile wall around his estate, eight feet tall at its lowest and rising to sixteen in places—thus becoming the first man ever to establish a bird sanctuary. He retained his interest in curare and we shall meet him briefly again.

chapter

7

Brodie and Waterton had now taught the essential lesson about curare. Between them, they had cemented into place a vital block in the Great Wall of medical knowledge. But as so often happens its importance to the whole structure was not immediately realized. Too much remained hidden from the investigators' eyes, and the "flying death" was slow to yield its secrets. No one even knew yet exactly what the poison was or which plants it came from. Neither did they know how it acted upon the body.

The first solutions to these problems were to be supplied during the next half century by two men who were both explorers, though in different ways. Sir Robert Schomburgk was a naturalist and surveyor who explored the unknown interior of British Guiana and charted its boundary with Venezuela. Claude Bernard was a physiologist who worked in a laboratory in Paris, and his explorations were carried out in the even more unknown interior of the human body.

Born in Prussia in 1804, Schomburgk lived most of his life in Britain or her overseas possessions. In the early 1830s, with an army officer as companion, he trekked into the wilderness regions along the upper Essequibo river, following in Waterton's footsteps. There he persuaded an Indian named Oronappi to take him to the place where the *"urari"* plant grew. It was a difficult journey, along steep jungle trails where the explorer often had to scramble on hands and knees over fallen trees and huge granite boulders. "The path was wretched," he wrote. "All traces of it were frequently lost, and an Indian only could have guided us; and he directed his course mostly by broken branches or marks cut in the trees, sometimes standing still for some moments to consider in which direction to turn." The party had to cross several streams meandering through deep gullies which in the rainy season would have been swollen into rushing rivers. "It appeared as if Nature here delighted only in gigantic forms," Schomburgk wrote. But at last their guide halted and waited for the white men to catch up. Then, pointing to "a ligneous twiner which wound itself snake-like from tree to tree," he cried out, *"Urari."*

Other travelers besides Waterton had described these bush-ropes but Schomburgk realized he was the first white man to look on one and know it was a source of the Indians' arrow poison. He was disappointed to find that it was not in flower, which would have assisted him in its identification. But he studied it long and carefully and in his description of it he wrote that it had a crooked stem, often more than three inches thick, with rough, dark gray bark, thin, climbing branches, and dark green leaves. Its fruit was "a berry the size of a large apple [which recalls Oviedo's speculation three centuries earlier about the fruit that brought all that trouble to Adam and Eve] covered with a smooth hard rind of a bluish-green colour and filled with a soft, jelly-like pulp, in which the seeds, ten to fifteen in number, are immersed."

Schomburgk concluded that the plant was, as von Humboldt had suggested, a member of the Strychnos group, of which there are more than three hundred species throughout the world. He named it *Strychnos toxifera* and it has since become one of the best-known sources of curare. Schomburgk was correct, but this identification was to cause some confusion in later years because the limp type of paralysis produced by curare is quite different from the violent muscular contractions caused by strychnine, the poison found in the seeds of an Indian tree which is also a variety of Strychnos, called *Nux vomica*.

To be certain the plant was really a source of curare, Schomburgk wanted to watch the poison being made. But at the last moment a neighboring chief arrived and forbade the poison-maker to prepare it in the presence of a white man. So Schomburgk took the samples of bark he had collected away with him and later soaked them in water for twenty-four hours, afterwards boiling the mixture down into a syrupy but not really thick extract of which he wrote: "It killed a fowl in twenty-seven minutes, although not sufficiently concentrated."

Had he concentrated his extract more, it would have killed the bird faster—but this did not matter. Schomburgk had proved at last that there was some substance locked in the bark of this one plant which, without the aid of snake venom or ant stings, would make a lethal curare. Later investigators have identified perhaps sixty different varieties of Strychnos in South America, and many of them have been used to make curare. But only one Strychnos plant growing elsewhere in the world, an African variety, has been found to have a curare action. Just why the New World species of Strychnos should contain a chemical substance with the unusual power to relax muscles so completely as to cause death is one of the endlessly fascinating enigmas of nature. Perhaps more remarkable still is the fact that this power is shared by a completely unrelated family of South American lianas. For Schomburgk's *Strychnos toxifera,* even though it was the first curare plant identified, is not the source of the curare used in modern medicine.

The curare used by Harold Griffith in 1942, and still used in operations today, comes from a climbing vine of the Moonseed family called *Chondodendron tomentosum.* The woody stem of this vine may climb a hundred feet to the canopy of the jungle or curl about on the ground in great rambling loops. At its base it is perhaps six inches thick, but the new shoots winding about the trees are only as thick as a pencil. The leaves of *Chondodendron tomentosum,* which grow only on new stems, are thick and leathery in texture, dark green above and almost white below. Some are close to heart-shape and others more like kidneys. Unlike the leaves, the tiny flowers and the grape-like clusters of fruit grow haphazardly on either old or new stems. The old wood, from which the plant-hunter must often make his identification, since leaves and flowers may be lost among the trees high above, is studded with wart-like growths marking old fruiting places. The fruit looks like an elongated Concord grape, but it is different inside, since it has only one seed, enclosed in a stone like that of a plum or peach. Though the wood is rich in the poison that makes curare, the bright red pulp round the stone of the fruit may be eaten.

The curare-producing varieties of Strychnos grow over a wide area of northern South America that takes in much of the Amazon and Orinoco basins and ranges from Guyana in the east to Peru in the west, and south from the isthmus of Panama almost to the northern border of Argentina. In comparison, the various Chondodendrons used to make curare have a more restricted distribution, being found in parts of Colombia, Ecuador, Peru, and western Brazil. The fiendishly complex problem facing those investigators who tried for years to analyze the composition of curare may be judged from the fact that one tribe might use several varieties of Strychnos in its poison, while another in a different area might use several types of Chondodendron. And just to complicate the issue further, in those places where the two families of plants grow side by side, both were sometimes thrown into the pot.

That the *Chondodendron tomentosum* vine was the one which eventually found its way into medical practice came about partly by chance and through the persistence of a twentieth-century American explorer we shall meet in a later chapter; partly because its poison is distributed throughout its wood, instead of only in its bark, so that one Chondodendron plant might yield more than a hundred pounds of raw material for the extraction process, while a Strychnos plant the same size might yield only a few pounds; and partly because it proved less difficult to isolate the alkaloids of *Chondodendron tomentosum* than those of *Strychnos toxifera*.

The term "alkaloid" is one that baffles laymen; perhaps the least intimidating way of defining it is to say that alkaloids are a class of chemical substances extracted mainly from plants but also from such diverse sources as bee stings, snake venoms, and coal tar. They are usually found in the form of salts, that is, united with some other substance. Scientists do not know how or why plants produce alkaloids. Most plants have none at all; others may yield twenty or more. There are at least 350,000

91

different species of plants throughout the world, and somewhere between ten and fifteen percent of them have been discovered to possess alkaloids. Some alkaloids are inert, or inactive, and are of interest only to research chemists. Others are the active principles of plants used medicinally for centuries, and among them are some of the most valuable drugs in use today.

The first alkaloid ever discovered, the potent pain-killing drug morphine, was isolated from opium in 1803 by a twenty-year-old apprentice apothecary, Friedrich Sertürner, in Germany. In later years, opium yielded many more alkaloids, including not only the notorious heroin but the much more innocuous codeine, which everyone has probably taken at some time or another in cough syrups or medicines to relieve the common cold. Other well-known alkaloids include quinine, which was isolated from the bark of the South American cinchona tree in 1820 and remained the only remedy for malaria until synthetic antimalarial drugs were introduced during World War II; caffeine, isolated from coffee, also in 1820, and used by doctors until quite recently to stimulate the heart rate and blood flow of patients half-dead from poisoning; atropine, extracted from the leaves and root of the deadly nightshade, or belladonna, and used by eye-doctors to dilate the pupil and by general practitioners in the treatment of whooping cough and asthma; and one of the best known of all alkaloids, nicotine, the active principle of tobacco.

Many other valuable drugs have come to us from the subtle world of the plants, and international drug companies spend hundreds of thousands of dollars every year seeking new ones, mounting expeditions to bring back botanical specimens and keeping batteries of chemists and pharmacologists at work in the laboratory on the delicate and time-consuming processes necessary to analyze them. The superiority of alkaloids over crude plant extracts is that since they are pure organic substances, uncontaminated by other compounds, they are constant and predictable in their action and can thus be prescribed with accuracy even though they may be deadly poisons if the safe dose is exceeded.

The botanical and chemical story of the curare lianas is infinitely complicated and still incomplete. A species of Chondodendron was first identified as a constituent of curare in 1846, but the alkaloid responsible for the poison's paralyzing action was not isolated from an authenticated specimen of *Chondo-*

dendron tomentosum until 1942—by which time the drug had already been used in the operating room. Between 1951 and 1963, the Russian-born Swiss chemist Paul Karrer, a Nobel Prize winner, discovered no fewer than twenty-four different alkaloids in samples of bark from Strychnos plants. The work continues in both Europe and America and new papers on it are published in scientific journals every year. But when Robert Schomburgk first saw the *"urari"* plant twisting up among the jungle trees and named it *Strychnos toxifera* all this was far off in the future. Other scientists in other fields had still to accomplish a task of research even more intricate and demanding than that faced by the botanists and chemists. The most important contribution to that task until modern times was made by Claude Bernard, son of a wine-grower and village schoolmaster in Saint-Julien in the Beaujolais region of France.

Born in 1813, Bernard was a quiet, serious boy who began his education at the age of eight by taking Latin lessons from the local priest. When he was eighteen, after several years at a Jesuit school, he was apprenticed to a pharmacist in Lyon, where his duties included sweeping the sidewalk, washing bottles, and making up shoe polish—the first "chemical" compound prepared by a boy who was to be honored in his later years as the father of experimental medicine. On the one evening off he enjoyed every month, Bernard haunted the local theater and soon, captivated by the bright world he saw beyond the pharmacist's counter, began to try his own hand at playwriting, poring over his manuscripts every night after the shop had closed. After eighteen months, M. Millet, the pharmacist, decided his young apprentice was spending too much time making up plots and not enough making up prescriptions, and fired him. Bernard left for Paris, armed with his latest work, a five-act tragedy involving the persecution of a handsome prince by his wicked uncle, the king. Fortunately for the future course of medicine, he was a flop as a dramatist and at the age of twenty-one he enrolled in medical school in Paris. At that time, physiology, the branch of biology concerned with the working of the living body, hardly existed as a separate science. It was taught as part of the science of anatomy, the study of the fundamental structure of the body rather than its living processes. Bernard enjoyed his anatomy lectures and became an artist at the dissection table, but as

93

might be expected of a frustrated playwright he was more fascinated by the mysteries of life than of death. Though he graduated as a doctor he never at any time went into practice but spent the whole of his illustrious career in the laboratory, devising and performing experiments on animals which laid the foundations of our modern understanding of the mechanism of the body.

Bernard is remembered today chiefly for his trail-blazing studies of the digestive processes and the nervous system. When he began his scientific career, the prevailing view was that the body's food needs were met by the mere breaking down—or burning up—of the substances eaten. No one had tried to understand what happened to different foods after they had entered the body; the most that had been attempted was a sort of inventory of what went in and what came out. Bernard considered this was "like trying to tell what happens inside a house by watching what goes in by the door and what comes out by the chimney." And, by meticulous experiments on living animals—for which he was often criticized, antivivisectionists being even more vocal in those days than now—he set about finding out what was going on inside the human house.

His first important discovery was the role played in digestion by the pancreas, the elongated organ lying behind the stomach which produces an alkaline juice that helps to break down the food we eat—proteins, carbohydrates, and fats—into a form suitable for use by the body. He also discovered what doctors call the glycogenic function of the liver—in other words, its ability to convert starch into glucose and store it until it is needed to supply energy. Bernard's researches into digestion showed that the body could create substances as well as merely consume them, and this paved the way for the eventual discovery of hormones.

The great achievement of Bernard's study of the body's nervous mechanism was his discovery of the vasomotor system, the network of nerves which governs the contraction and dilation of the blood vessels and thus regulates the supply of blood to every organ of the body. This alone would have been enough to win him an enduring place in the history of neurological investigation. His experiments with curare, while they did not contribute directly to this work, supplied the impetus for a whole

94

series of inquiries, which are still going on, into how the minute electrical charges generated within the brain act on chemical substances to control our bodily activity.

Bernard became interested in curare in the early 1840s and obtained samples of it from several returned explorers. Since the Indians ate the meat of animals killed by poisoned arrows without any ill effects and even on occasion took curare as a remedy—probably more fancied than real—for stomach ailments, the belief had grown up that it was harmless when taken into the stomach. Bernard mixed curare with the food of dogs and rabbits and demonstrated that this was a mistaken assumption. But since the poison was absorbed more slowly through the digestive tract than through the blood, much larger quantities could safely be eaten than could be injected into the bloodstream— as the Abbé Fontana had said in the previous century.

In further experiments on frogs Bernard confirmed that the poison did not affect the heart, and he became the first investigator to spell out the sequence in which it paralyzed the muscles. He pricked "a dog of gentle disposition" with a poisoned arrow and watched it die. It wagged its tail to the last. Then he sacrificed another dog with "a ferocious nature" and found that even as it became paralyzed it continued to growl at anyone who came near and when threatened with a stick "bit it with strength and silent rage." From these experiments he concluded that curare did not destroy the intelligence, since each animal retained its character to the last. This living death, which seemed so calm and painless, was thus "the most atrocious suffering that the human imagination can conceive."

The great experimenter then turned his attention to curare's effect on the brain, if any, and the nervous system. The nerves that enable us to feel pain, or heat, or cold, the grasp of a handshake or even the wisp of a feather brushed against the skin, are called the sensory nerves. They begin just beneath the skin as millions of infinitesimal branches which, to pursue the analogy of a tree, converge on larger branches and eventually into the main trunk of the nerve. Each of these nerves, however fine, shares with telephone wires the property of conducting impulses. The skin is so liberally laced with minute sensory nerves that whether the impulse—doctors call it the stimulus—is applied in the form of a sharp pinprick or the blunt whack of a paddle, the brain knows a split second later exactly where the stimulus was applied and over what area.

Impulses conducted along the sensory nerves travel inward from the surface of the skin toward the brain. If they demand some form of action, other nerves are called into play. If some overenthusiastic greeter grips your hand too heartily, for instance, you immediately wince and try to pull it away. Or if you are walking barefoot through the grass and you step on a thorn, you promptly lift your foot and, if the thorn remains embedded in the flesh, reach down to pull it out with your fingers. All these motions are accomplished by muscles, and the nerves which govern the muscles form a network called the motor system, entirely separate from the sensory system. The impulses that travel along the motor nerves originate in the brain—or in the case of a reflex action in nerve centers in the spinal cord—and travel outward to various parts of the body. But their destination is not the skin. The motor nerves end in the muscles and the impulses they transmit cause the muscles to contract.

Reflex actions are carried out independently of the brain by what are known as reflex arcs, and there are many thousands of reflex arcs in the human body. They all involve sensory nerves, nerve centers in the spinal cord, and motor nerves. To go back to that painful moment when your bare foot came down on a thorn, the sudden stimulus is conducted along the tiniest sensory nerves until they swell like a river fed by tributaries into the plantar nerve, which in turn is joined by other nerves on its journey up the leg until it reaches the spinal cord by way of the sciatic nerve, the main nerve trunk in the leg, which is about the thickness of your thumb. Even though nerve impulses travel almost instantaneously, this sudden emergency demands the swiftest possible motor action, so without waiting for instructions from the brain, the spinal nerve center flashes a message along the motor nerves, which contract the muscles in your leg and cause you to pick up your foot before you have even realized you are going to do it. This is a reflex action. Your foot is now off the ground and even though you may be hopping around with the thorn still stuck there, it may no longer be painful, so that the sensory nerves may have ceased to transmit evidence of its presence. However, you must still get rid of it, by plucking it out. This subsequent action of your muscles is initiated by the brain, through the motor nerves, independently of the sensory system.

This separate functioning of the sensory and motor nerves enabled Bernard to make a vital discovery—the site of curare's action on the body. He first tied a thread tightly around the left hind leg of a frog, compressing the artery and vein in the thigh so that no blood could pass between that leg and the rest of the body. Then he injected curare under the skin of the frog's back. Within twenty minutes the frog was paralyzed—except for its left leg, which the blood, and hence the poison carried by it, had been unable to reach. In turn, Bernard pinched the skin of the frog's back, its forefeet, and its right hind leg. None of these parts moved. But each time he pinched a paralyzed part the unpoisoned leg twitched in a reflex action. The frog could thus feel the stimulus all over its body, but could respond to it only in the unparalyzed leg. The sensory nerves, therefore, were unaffected by the curare; their messages were still getting through to the nerve centers. But somehow the poison was preventing the motor nerves from moving the muscles in the paralyzed areas.

Where was the block taking place? Was it in the brain? In the motor nerves themselves? Or in the muscles? Bernard now went a step further. He made an incision in a frog's leg and, with the delicate skill he had learned at the dissecting table, divided it so that he could tie off the blood vessels but leave the nerves connected to the rest of the body. If the curare acted on the brain, or on the motor nerves, the tied-off leg, even though he was now sure no poison could reach it in the blood, should be paralyzed in the same way as the rest of the body.

It wasn't. The results were the same as before. When the paralyzed parts of the frog were pinched, the tied-off limb jerked. So nerve impulses were still able to pass through the paralyzed part of the body into the unparalyzed leg. Furthermore, with the nerves of the unpoisoned leg exposed, Bernard was able to stimulate them with a small electric charge. The charge passed down the nerve and the muscles contracted as usual. He deduced from this that the curare acted not on the brain or the motor nerves themselves, but somewhere near the periphery or outer edge of the system.

Now he made another discovery. He cut open the lower parts of both hind legs and applied his electric current to the calf muscles. There was virtually no difference between the contraction of the muscle in the paralyzed right leg and that in the unparalyzed left. This suggested that the muscles themselves were not paralyzed, so he undertook yet another series of experiments. Muscle tissue taken from the body after death retains its "irritability," or power to contract, for some time. Bernard removed the calf muscles, with part of their nerves still attached, from another frog. He placed the nerve of one muscle in a dish containing a solution of curare, but left the muscle outside it. When he stimulated the nerve, even though it was immersed in the paralyzing curare, the muscle moved. So the curare had no effect on the nerve. Now he put the other muscle in the curare solution, but left the nerve outside. This time, when he stimulated the nerve, there was no answering movement of the muscle. So was it the muscle that was paralyzed after all? He left the muscle in the curare, and applied the electric current to it directly. The charge galvanized it into life as though the curare had not been there.

At last he had found his answer. In his quiet laboratory thousands of miles from the jungles where the poison vines fastened their twisting embrace on the trees and where the naked hunters crouched over their bubbling pots, Claude Bernard, frustrated playwright but brilliant physiologist, had discovered the long-hidden secret of the "flying death." There could be only one explanation: curare paralyzed neither the nerves nor the muscles, so it must somehow disrupt the connection between them.

Neither Bernard nor anyone else at that time knew what shape this connection between the nerves and the muscles took. During the next century, innumerable investigators inspired by Bernard's work sought to explain the phenomenon without success. Only in recent years, since the introduction of the electron microscope has enabled biological researchers to measure in ten-millionths of a millimeter, have we attained our present incomplete understanding of the intricate process involved. Muscles consist of millions of tough little fibers and for a muscle to contract it is necessary for each of these fibers to become shorter and thicker. The signal that causes them to change their shape comes to them from the ends of the motor nerves. The point at which a nerve ending meets a muscle is now known as the "myoneural junction," and it is the complex electrochemical process occurring at this junction that is disrupted by curare.

If you decide to lift your foot off the floor, your brain sends a series of tiny electrical impulses—hundreds of them per second —down the motor nerves to the muscles which must contract to enable you to perform the movement. With suitable amplifying equipment, these signals can be heard; they sound like the crackling of a Geiger counter held near a source of radioactivity. But it is not electricity as such that causes the muscle fibers to change their shape; it is a chemical process.

At the myoneural junction there is a chemical substance called "acetylcholine" which, when the muscle is at rest, is inactive, its molecules being split into two. When the motor nerve discharges its electrical impulses into the acetylcholine, the split molecules immediately join up into their active form. In their new shape, they fit snugly into minute depressions in special cells of the muscle fibers called "end plates," and there they initiate the chemical process that causes the fibers to contract.

The molecules of curare are very similar in shape to the linked-up molecules of acetylcholine and when they arrive at the myoneural junction they behave like squatters taking over an unoccupied building: they move into the depressions, called "receptors," in the muscle end plates. While they fit comfortably into the receptors, they are unable because of their different composition to initiate the chemical process that causes the muscles to contract. But as long as they stay there they prevent the lawful tenants, the acetylcholine molecules, from entering. The muscles thus remain relaxed, however many anguished signals arrive at the myoneural junction ordering them to contract.

The situation at the end plates is not a static one. The molecules, whether of acetylcholine or curare, do not settle permanently into the receptors in the muscle fibers, but mill around bombarding them. Paralysis takes place when the acetylcholine molecules are heavily outnumbered and cannot get through to the receptors.

However, no matter how successful their initial bombardment may be, the curare molecules are helpless against counterattack by the body's natural chemical defenses. Given time, the defenders are always able to surround and wipe out the invaders. But if the curare molecules have gained entry to the body in sufficient

99

numbers, that time—as Brodie and Waterton demonstrated—can only be provided by artificial respiration.

Claude Bernard knew nothing of this microscopic contest of the molecules, but his discovery that curare broke the connection between the nerves and the muscles established the basis not only for the later study of the drug but for the furtherance of human understanding of the way the nervous system works. Largely as a result of Bernard's work, curare became a tool for physiological research and for the instruction of medical students, which was its chief use up to 1942. The peculiar form of relaxed paralysis it induces turned experimental animals into immobile living laboratories where the functions of the body could be studied. As Bernard wrote, curare enabled the physiologist "to dissociate and analyze the most delicate phenomena of the living organism, and by studying attentively the mechanism of death he indirectly learns about the physiological mechanism of life."

Since Bernard himself had pointed out that curare did not interfere with feeling or intelligence, its use in this way certainly involved some cruelty—though probably less than some of his other experiments, one of which called for the roasting alive of a rabbit to see what temperature would prove fatal. Madame Bernard objected strenuously to his vivisection and made frequent donations to a French society devoted to the protection of animals.

In England, too, the growing number of experiments performed on living animals aroused a public outcry. In 1875 the government appointed a Royal Commission to investigate the situation, which resulted in a law banning vivisection. And a few years later Lord Tennyson, the poet laureate, lashed out poetically at any doctor who would consent to see the dog that had fawned at his knee "drenched with hellish *oorali.*"

Bernard's justification for his experiments was typically straightforward: "Man, who has the right to use animals for domestic purposes and his food, is equally entitled to use them in order to inform himself in a science useful to mankind."

chapter

8

One winter evening in 1839 a police inspector named Phelps was patrolling the streets of Nottingham, England, when he heard a dog barking and howling in obvious fear. Upon investigation, in the policeman's time-honored phrase, he discovered a pointer trapped at the foot of an excavation being dug to house the foundations of a public weighing machine. Inspector Phelps, who appears to have shared his countrymen's well-known solicitude for animals, found a ladder, descended into the hole, and picked up the frightened dog in his arms. Unfortunately his humanitarianism exceeded his caution: as he regained street level the dog bit him on the nose and upper lip and then scampered off yelping into the night.

Six weeks later, Inspector Phelps fell ill. He told a friend he thought he must be going mad and went to see his doctor. As he walked into the examination room, he caught sight of water running from a tap into a washbasin in the corner of the room —and immediately collapsed in an uncontrollable convulsion.

In response to the doctor's urgent messages, the leading medical men of the city rushed to his assistance. By the time they arrived it was clear that Inspector Phelps was in the throes of that dreaded disease known as hydrophobia. All agreed there was nothing they could do. Or was there? Among the assembled dignitaries was one Francis Sibson, M.D., resident surgeon to the Nottingham General Hospital. Sibson had a friend who believed he knew a remedy for hydrophobia. A messenger was sped off to summon this last hope—none other than the gentle reader's good friend, Charles Waterton, Squire of nearby Walton Hall.

Waterton had been awaiting this chance for years. Pausing long enough only to snatch up a ball of *wourali* coated with wax, he hastened off to Nottingham. He was too late. By the time he got there Phelps had died, in terrible agony—and the Squire was denied the distinction of becoming the first man to attempt to use curare in the treatment of human disease.

If the idea that such a sinister poison could be transformed into a medicine seems rash, it must be remembered that South America had bestowed more than gold and tobacco and potatoes on the Old World. Throughout the years it had come to be considered a treasure house of medicinal virtues. Quinine was only one among dozens of South American substances with real or imagined value to the doctors of Waterton's day.

There was *ipecacuanha,* which an eighteenth-century English buccaneer and ship's doctor named Thomas Dover compounded with opium and sold as "Dover's powder"; *ipecacuanha* yields an alkaloid called emetine which is still employed, among other things, in the treatment of amoebic dysentery. There was *guaiac,* once thought to be a cure for syphilis and still approved for the treatment of rheumatism; sarsparilla, a popular "tonic" on both sides of the Atlantic during the last century, which was later found to contain an element similar to testosterone, the male sex hormone; cascara, jalap, and many others. And after Waterton's day, the leaves of the South American coca tree were to give medicine another priceless boon, the local anesthetic cocaine.

Like all these valuable medicines, curare came from a South American plant; perhaps it too possessed the hidden power to heal. What if it *was* a deadly poison? Doctors used many substances which, if prescribed in overdoses, were deadly poisons. Besides, in the donkey Wouralia, still "fat and frisky" in the grounds of Walton Hall, Waterton had a living reminder of the key fact about curare: that its effect could be counteracted by artificial respiration. And so the Squire and his friend Dr. Sibson set off several times to try to cure cases of hydrophobia with curare, in the hope that the relaxed form of paralysis it induces might eliminate the dreadful convulsions that accompany the disease. They were never able to test their theory, because the patients invariably died before they could reach them.

Unlike his friend the Squire, Sibson was by no means an eccentric. He was a man of wide interests and genuine achievements, and perhaps his friendship with Waterton was founded on a mutual passion for nature study, since one of his early publications was entitled "On the Blowhole of the Porpoise." After thirteen years in Nottingham, Sibson went to London and earned lasting recognition for his contribution to the understanding of the functioning of the internal organs. But neither Sibson nor Waterton originated the idea that curare might help victims of hydrophobia. That came from William Sewell, the veterinary professor who had assisted Benjamin Brodie in the operation on Wouralia. When he saw how curare paralyzed all the donkey's muscles, Sewell suggested it might be valuable in the treatment of two diseases which cause violent muscular contractions: hydrophobia and tetanus. He was wrong in the first case, but right in the second—though curare did not successfully take its present place in the treatment of tetanus until after its use in anesthesia had taught doctors how to control it.

Hydrophobia is such a terrible disease that Waterton's anxiety to try to cure it with his *wourali* is understandable. But once it takes hold of the body it is incurable, even today. Transmitted to man by the bite of an animal with rabies, hydrophobia is in medical terms an acute inflammation of the brain and the rest of the central nervous system. This is an entirely inadequate description of its horrors. Before he is released by death, the victim of hydrophobia suffers hours or even days of unimaginable agony.

The virus, contained in the animal's saliva, takes some time to establish itself in the body. Usually the symptoms begin to show from two to six weeks after the bite, though there is one case in the records of the World Health Organization in which they did not appear for 346 days—almost a year. In the early stages of the disease, the patient becomes depressed and is bothered by headaches and loss of appetite. He can't sleep and is oppressed by a sense of danger. He becomes ultrasensitive

103

to bright lights or loud noises, and he may find difficulty in swallowing.

As the disease progresses, his sensitivity reaches the point of mania. The slightest outside influence—some small noise, an unexpected draft of air—may throw him into excruciating convulsions. Worst of all, the mere attempt to drink a glass of water provokes an uncontrollable fear and painful spasms of the throat —it is this dread of water that gives the disease its name in man. The torture is ended only when the exhausted victim lapses into unconsciousness, and then death.

Hydrophobia was recognized by the ancients and Pliny the Elder, mother lode of folk remedies, suggested it could be cured by the liver of a mad dog. Pliny notwithstanding, there was absolutely no defense against the disease until 1885, when Pasteur, whose bacteriological discoveries inspired Lister to introduce antisepsis, discovered that from the dried spinal cords of infected rabbits he could prepare a vaccine which, if administered soon enough after the bite, would prevent development of the disease.

It was one of the most dramatic victories ever won over a disease. People who had been bitten by rabid animals converged on Paris for treatment from all over Europe. The *New York Herald* raised enough money by public subscription to send four American children who had been bitten by rabid dogs to Pasteur. All were saved. Next to arrive were nineteen Russians who had been savagely mauled by a mad wolf that had wandered around for two days and nights, attacking everyone it came across. At that time, eighty-two out of every hundred people bitten by rabid wolves died. Pasteur saved sixteen of the nineteen wounded Russians, even though they had not arrived in Paris until two weeks after they were bitten.

Prompt inoculation against hydrophobia is still essential for anyone bitten by an animal suspected of being rabid. And rabies is still a serious threat in parts of the world, though some countries, such as Britain, have managed to eradicate it by stringent quarantine regulations. In 1966 the World Health Organization issued a warning that a widespread outbreak of the disease had flared up among wild animals in Europe, Asia, Africa, and the Americas. Rabies seems to occur in cycles and there was a similar world-wide epidemic a century ago. Wild animals susceptible to it include wolves, coyotes, foxes, jackals, skunks, mongooses, weasels, and bats. It is spread to humans mostly by dogs and cats which have not been immunized against it. A W.H.O. survey disclosed that there were 1453 human victims of hydrophobia in ninety-seven countries during 1962. In that same year, almost half a million people who had been bitten received vaccine treatment. The figures did not include the Soviet Union and mainland China. Tragically, even people inoculated after bites occasionally contract the disease. In Canada, in 1967, a four-year-old girl bitten by a cat three months earlier died even though she had received the course of injections—and her mother and two other people bitten at the same time endured months of anxiety until it was clear they were out of danger. In countries that replied to a W.H.O. questionnaire, there were 124 deaths during or after treatment in the two years 1960 and 1961.

Since hydrophobia was such a scourge and no known treatment for it was the slightest use before Pasteur's vaccine, it is strange that mere desperation did not prompt others besides Waterton and Sibson to take up Sewell's suggestion that curare might cure it. But Waterton's fruitless dash to the side of Inspector Phelps in Nottingham seems to have aroused little interest and no emulation. Twenty years later, in 1859, Sibson told a meeting of the Royal Medical and Chirurgical Society he still thought the idea had promise, though the administration of curare would undoubtedly call for artificial respiration. He had, in fact, kept the necessary apparatus ready for many years in case there had been an opportunity to try the treatment.

Again, no one seemed interested. It was a further seventeen years before a brief paragraph appeared in the British medical journal *The Lancet,* reporting without details that a Berlin doctor named Offenberg had successfully treated a case of hydrophobia with a hypodermic injection of curare. In that same year—1876—Dr. B. A. Watson, surgeon to the Jersey City Charity Hospital, wrote in the *American Journal of Medical Science* claiming a similar success.

Watson's patient was a strong, able-bodied man of forty-five, "of temperate and industrious habits," who had been bitten by a pet Newfoundland dog. His servant girl, bitten at the same time, had died of hydrophobia. When Watson saw the man in hospital he had a severe chill and was retching. Watson treated the "paroxysms" he developed during the next few days with minute quantities of strychnine—then the accepted form of treatment—but when this could no longer be given because of the patient's vomiting he tried an injection of curare. Twenty minutes later, the man, who had been babbling wildly, fell asleep. When he awoke, Watson repeated the injection—"and he has had no return of the symptoms from that day to this."

Since the man recovered, it seems likely that he did not have hydrophobia at all. Watson recognized this possibility—he called it "a supposed case of rabies canina"—but seems to have thought that the illness was genuine and that the curare had cured it. In those days, people bitten by rabid dogs lived in so much dread of hydrophobia that they sometimes developed what was called pseudohydrophobia, or lyssophobia, a hysterical conviction that they were going to die from the disease. This conviction was accompanied by symptoms very similar to those of the disease itself, right down to the fear of water.

Whether Watson's patient really had hydrophobia or not, there was still no sign of curare being used for the disease in England. In 1878 an apparently rabid dog—a cross between a St. Bernard and a collie—tore its kennel to pieces, snapped its chain, and ran amok near Bagshot, in southern England. It bit three children, burst into a cottage and bit the woman occupant on the breast, and then attacked a woodman who, though bitten, managed to kill it with a pitchfork.

Reporting this incident, *The Lancet* said in an editorial that it was "most desirable" that, if any cases of hydrophobia resulted from the attack, "a thorough trial of curara [sic] should be made." It was, the anonymous writer added, "remarkable that this supposed remedy does not seem to have been tried in any case in this country since its alleged effects became known."

Fortunately, the bitten people seemed to escape the disease—or at any rate their fate was not reported to *The Lancet*. But the editorial did elicit a letter from a doctor in practice in Waterton's old stamping-ground, Demerara, who said he had used the treatment a few months earlier on a nine-year-old boy. Having jabbed the boy in the back with two curare-laden arrows, without apparent effect, the doctor stabbed him a third time. Predictably, the boy now "expired." Such drastic therapeutic measures could hardly be considered either a fair or a conclusive trial of William Sewell's proposed remedy, but no one else seems to have followed it up. Even had they done so, curare could not have saved hydrophobia victims, though it might have eased their passing by alleviating their convulsions. Nowadays, this is accomplished by other drugs.

Sewell's second suggestion, that curare might help in the treatment of tetanus, received a much wider response. Attempts to use it in this way were made, though without much success, right up to the time when its introduction to anesthesia demonstrated how it could be handled with safety. Tetanus, better known as lockjaw, is sometimes dismissed today as one of those diseases people *used* to suffer from, in the bad old days. This is a dangerous misconception. While it is undoubtedly much less common than it used to be in industrial countries, tetanus still kills more than fifty thousand people a year throughout the world—more, according to World Health Organization statistics, than are killed by smallpox, plague, or poliomyelitis and many other diseases that receive far more attention. Even with modern methods of treatment, if you catch tetanus in the United States your chances of surviving are less than fifty-fifty. There were 322 cases of the disease in the United States in 1962, with 215 deaths—a mortality rate of 66.7 percent. And death from tetanus is hardly less horrible than death from hydrophobia.

The onset of the disease is signaled by a slight feeling of stiffness in the neck or jaws, and perhaps difficulty in chewing food. Gradually the muscles of the jaws tighten up until the victim can no longer open his mouth. The paralysis may affect the whole face, raising the eyebrows and the corners of the mouth in a macabre expression so well known that there is a medical term to describe it: the *risus sardonicus,* or sardonic grin. As more muscles are affected the victim is twisted by ghastly convulsions. His teeth clenched, sweat pouring from his tortured body, he writhes helplessly in contortions that are terrible to watch. Sometimes his back is so agonizingly arched that only his head and heels touch the ground. These convulsions may last seconds, or they may drag on for minutes. They are so violent that the unnatural stresses sometimes tear the large abdominal muscles reaching from the ribs down to the groin. They usually end in death from heart failure or suffocation.

The organism responsible for this terrible suffering is a widespread bacillus known as *Clostridium tetani,* which lives in soil, garden mold, and the intestines of many animals, particularly horses and cows and including a few human carriers. Soil which has been farmed for generations and fertilized by animal manure is thus especially rich in the bacilli, but they also exist elsewhere. Some areas are particularly noted for the presence of the bacillus: the special patch of earth used to coat arrows by the natives of the New Hebrides is an example. By an unpleasant coincidence, the island of St. Kilda in the original Hebrides, off the northern coast of Scotland, used to be notorious for tetanus. During one period, before modern methods of hygiene were introduced, eighty-four out of 125 children born on the island died of tetanus within fourteen days of their birth, because of infection contracted when their umbilical cords were cut.

The bacillus enters the body through wounds, even slight ones such as scratches caused by thorns or sore spots produced by a nail sticking up through a shoe. The disease also used to be spread in hospitals by the presence of the bacilli in catgut used to stitch wounds, or contaminated dressings. It is still common among newborn children in primitive areas of the world where the umbilical cord is cut by an unsterilized knife or the rusty lid of a can and mud or dung is plastered on the wound to stop the bleeding.

Clostridium tetani has a spore, which, when deprived of oxygen, as it is in the dead tissues of a wound, germinates and produces a virulent toxin, or poison. Whereas the fatal dose of strychnine for a man of about 155 pounds varies from thirty to a hundred milligrams, one-fifth of a milligram of tetanus toxin can be fatal. The poison is absorbed by the end plates of the muscles and from there it creeps upward through the motor nerves to the spinal cord. The human body has no natural defenses, or antibodies, against the toxin, but it can be prompted to manufacture them by injections of either minute quantities of the toxin itself or of antibodies produced in horses. This potentially fatal disease can thus be prevented by inoculation. British and American troops were protected against it routinely during World War II and rarely caught it. German and Japanese forces, who were not so well protected, suffered many casualties from it. It is routine in the emergency wards of modern hospitals for accident victims to be given antitetanus "shots" on admission.

Curare, of course, cannot cure tetanus, but it can when used with proper safeguards control the convulsions and prevent them from exhausting or killing the patient while he is treated by other means. As a veterinarian, Sewell twice tried to use the drug to save horses suffering from tetanus—animals can contract the disease as well as carry it. Both horses died, one of them after four hours of artificial respiration, but Sewell was satisfied that they had died from tetanus and not from the effects of the curare.

The first recorded attempt to use curare on a human patient with tetanus was made on New Year's Eve, 1857, by Dr. Lewis A. Sayre, professor of orthopedic surgery at Bellevue Hospital, in New York City. Bellevue then, as now, was one of the city's leading hospitals and Sayre, a distinguished writer on medical topics, was among the doctors who attended William Morton, the discoverer of anesthesia, in his last illness. The patient to whom he gave curare, an Irish laborer named Owen Daly, had been climbing a ladder when it slipped and fell. In grabbing for something to hold on to, Daly ripped his hand on a nail. Eleven days later he was admitted to Bellevue with stiffness in his neck and jaw muscles. Sayre amputated his thumb in an attempt to stop the poison spreading up the nerves to the spinal cord, but it was already too late.

As Daly grew worse and the typical tetanus spasms spread through his muscles "it was considered that this was a fit case for the administration of the *woorari* poison, from its well-known power of bringing on muscular relaxation." Sayre dissolved some curare in water and applied it to the wound on a pad of lint at 8 P.M. on New Year's Eve. He stayed with the patient all night, repeating the doses of curare, but at 4:15 A.M. on January 1 Daly died in "a very intense spasm involving the whole body."

In his account of the case, Sayre drew no conclusions and did not speculate about the potential worth of the treatment. However, others took up where he left off. The following year, Sir Thomas Spencer Wells, an English surgeon who had served with distinction in the navy and on the battlefields of the Crimea and was thus no stranger to tetanus, used curare to treat three woman suffering from the disease.

Wells became famous as a pioneer of surgery within the abdomen by perfecting a daring operation first performed many years earlier by Ephraim McDowell, a backwoods surgeon who

109

traveled on horseback through the countryside around Danville, Kentucky, operating singlehandedly in isolated cabins, with the patient's relatives or friends as his only assistants. One day in December 1809 McDowell was summoned by a country woman named Jane Todd Crawford, who thought she was pregnant. His examination convinced McDowell that what Mrs. Crawford expected to be her sixth child was actually a huge growth on her ovary which would soon kill her, since no surgeon at that time would risk cutting into the abdomen to attempt to cure such a condition.

The rigors of their practice, however, bred self-reliance in those old frontier doctors and McDowell was convinced that since the spaying operations performed on animals involved opening the abdomen, in theory at least it should be possible to duplicate them in humans. Without mincing words, he explained the situation to Mrs. Crawford: she could stay in the cabin with her husband and children and resign herself to certain death, or she could come to Danville for an operation which was only an experiment and which might kill her even more quickly than the tumor. A true pioneer, she chose the operation. Reading about the case today, one marvels that she survived the four-day ride to Danville, let alone the surgery: the enormous tumor hung down almost to her knees and must have been buffeted painfully —and dangerously—against the saddle. But she stuck it out and reached McDowell's house, where he made her rest for a few days to get over her soreness.

Then, on Christmas Day, the backwoods surgeon performed a feat that is one of the landmarks of surgical progress. He could not give his patient anything to kill her pain, since Morton's demonstration of ether was still almost forty years in the future. So, while Jane recited psalms to bolster her resolution, McDowell cut into her swollen abdomen and removed a tumor weighing more than twenty-two pounds. The operation lasted twenty-five minutes, but those twenty-five tortured minutes gave Jane Crawford a further thirty-two years of life. They also brought Ephraim McDowell lasting fame. He was the first surgeon to perform an ovariectomy, the removal of an ovary, and his operation is widely considered the forerunner of modern abdominal surgery.

An indication of the magnitude of McDowell's achievement is the fact that fifty years later, when the experienced Spencer

110

Wells first saw an ovariectomy performed in England—this time with anesthesia—he distrusted the operation because of its severity and because the patient died. Later, convinced of its value, he himself performed it more than a thousand times, though it was not generally accepted by the British medical profession until 1864.

Two of the patients whose tetanus Spencer Wells treated with curare were women whose ovaries he had removed. The third was a woman he had treated for a prolapsed, or fallen, womb. Reporting on these cases in 1859, he seemed puzzled that they had all occurred in his practice within a month, when for ten years before that he had never seen a case of tetanus. Before ten more years had elapsed Joseph Lister supplied a possible explanation—with his paper on the necessity for antisepsis in the operating room.

Spencer Wells's first patient had developed the spasms of tetanus two weeks after the ovariectomy. He administered the curare by hypodermic injection and in six days the woman recovered. The other two women died—one of them on the very evening that he described the cases to the Royal Medical and Chirurgical Society. Nevertheless, he thought the fact that one of three patients had survived sufficiently encouraging to warrant further investigation of the treatment. Such was "the very fatal nature" of tetanus that deaths from it should not discourage trials of curare's effectiveness.

Earlier in that same year of 1859, an Italian physiologist and surgeon named Vella, who had studied under Claude Bernard, used curare to treat three soldiers wounded at the Battle of Magenta, where the Sardinians and their French allies defeated the Austrians in one of the many engagements that preceded the unification of Italy. Two of the soldiers were already near death when the curare was applied to their wounds, and though it did not save them it gave them, in the words of a contemporary report, "a certain amount of muscular relaxation and general relief." The third case was a French sergeant, wounded in the foot by a rifle ball. Three days after the ball had been removed his jaw tightened and he went into tetanic convulsions. After the administration of curare, he was able to drink and sit up in bed and he eventually recovered—though whether he really owed his survival to the curare we shall never know.

111

For the next eighty years, sporadic efforts continued to be made to harness the "flying death" in the service of medicine. Dozens of papers were published discussing its value in tetanus, particularly in France, where Bernard's experiments had proved a tremendous stimulus to research and where attempts were also made to use the drug to control the involuntary muscular contractions of such conditions as epilepsy and St. Vitus's dance. But the results of later investigators were scarcely more encouraging than those of Spencer Wells and Vella. The way ahead was still barred by two obstacles that seemed insuperable, obstacles that were outlined in an editorial in *The Lancet* commenting on Vella's experience.

"It is one of the least promising characteristics of curare," this said, "that both in its composition and effect it is uncertain and varying. Its chemical nature is not uniform, even its source is variable, and its energies are unequal in various specimens. If it were possible to distil a yet more deadly poison from this most poisonous drug, and to extract from it *curarina* as its active alkaloid, a fixed intensity might be attained . . . Experiments upon animals have shown that after the tetanic spasms have ceased, perhaps controlled by the action of the curare, death has followed apparently from paralysis of the organs of respiration, so that the surgeon has the satisfaction of thinking that if he saves his patient from the disease, he may kill him by the remedy."

The unpredictable action of the various samples of curare finding their way to Europe at that time, and the genuine difficulties faced by those chemists who tried to isolate their alkaloids, have already been mentioned. But it is one of the enduring mysteries of the curare story that with the lesson of Waterton and Brodie before them—not only in medical papers but in one of the best-selling travel books of the era—so many investigators should have been both surprised and deterred from further inquiry by the poison's paralyzing effect on the muscles controlling breathing. Certainly, the management of adequate artificial respiration was a hazardous proceeding in the days of Spencer Wells. But respiratory paralysis caused investigators to write off curare as too dangerous for use in humans right up until its successful introduction to the operating room—and even afterwards.

As late as 1952 the authoritative British Encyclopedia of Medical Practice, in an article on tetanus, said: "At present there is no preparation of curarine which is reliable and safe, chiefly because the margin between the dose needed to produce muscular relaxation and control of convulsions and that which will cause a dangerous paralysis of respiratory muscles is too small." At that time, curare had been in use in the operating room for ten years.

The lack of a pure curare alkaloid was a more understandable brake on research. A "bitter principle" was extracted from a sample of the poison as early as 1827 by Jean Baptiste Boussingault, a French chemist sent out to Colombia by von Humboldt, at the request of the liberator Simón Bolívar, to establish a scientific institute at Bogotá. This was not a pure alkaloid and since it had a pronounced tendency to absorb moisture from the atmosphere, which made for further variations in its strength, it was not much of an improvement on the raw curare for medical purposes.

Toward the end of the nineteenth century, a German doctor named Rudolf Boehm who had abandoned the practice of psychiatry for the research laboratory of the pharmacologist thought he had hit upon a method of classifying the various curares. The poison reached Europe in three types of native container: hollow lengths of bamboo tube sealed at each end with skins; clay pots; and gourds or calabashes. Boehm believed each type of container came from a different region and would therefore be packed with poison prepared from a different species of plant. He analyzed samples from the three types of container and isolated what he thought were pure alkaloids from each. The substance he obtained from calabash-curare he called curarine; that from tube-curare, tubocurarine; and from pot-curare, protocurarine.

Unfortunately the chemical formulas he assigned to these substances turned out to be erroneous, and later travelers cast doubt on his whole classification system by pointing out that all three types of containers were found in the same regions and which one was used was largely a matter of convenience for the Indian poison-maker. But imperfect though Boehm's classification system was, it did represent an advance on the previous confusion and his curarine was the nearest thing to a pure alkaloid available to investigators until the 1930s, when a brilliant British research chemist named Harold King supplied the first glimmer of light at the end of the centuries-long tunnel.

Harold King was born in 1887 and grew up in the pleasant seaside resort of Bangor, in North Wales, where both his father and mother were school teachers. As a boy, he was shy and studious and though he was interested in science generally he began to specialize in chemistry only at the suggestion of a fellow student. He graduated from the university with first-class honors and spent virtually his whole career in the laboratories of Britain's National Institute for Medical Research. King was the epitome of the devoted scientist, and few outside interests drew him away from his laboratory for long. He left Britain only twice in his life—once for a short holiday in Ireland and once during World War II when, as secretary of the committee set up to supervise the production of penicillin, he had to fly to the United States. After his retirement, he collected and studied butterflies with the same intensity he had applied to his chemical researches.

Rarely spectacular—the patient labors of research chemists seldom are—King's basic studies made many indirect contributions to medicine. Early in his career, the outbreak of World War I cut off Britain's supply of products from the German drug factories, upon which she was heavily dependent, and he was pitchforked into the desperate effort to establish a domestic industry for the manufacture of synthetic drugs. One of his achievements was to develop a process for the production of the lowly but indispensable aspirin tablet, hitherto imported from the Bayer company in Germany. He carried out basic research on many other drugs and between the wars managed to synthesize in the laboratory several alkaloids with actions similar to that of quinine. His groundwork proved invaluable later when the United States instituted the crash program to develop synthetic antimalaria drugs during World War II. He also made a vital theoretical contribution to the early chemical work on cholesterol which ultimately led to revolutionary discoveries in the field of human hormones.

When King embarked on his study of curare no one could have foreseen its eventual importance to anesthesia. But curiously enough he had made earlier contributions to this branch of the medical arts, notably his purification of an anesthetic agent called diethyl ether. His interest in the "flying death" was awakened by the work of his chief, Sir Henry H. Dale, former director of the National Institute for Medical Research and one of Britain's most eminent twentieth-century scientists. Dale spent many years unraveling the mysteries of the chemical process by which nerve impulses are transmitted to muscles. Since curare was known to disrupt this process somehow, it was a natural field of investigation.

The labyrinthine procedures used by organic chemists to break down materials into their basic constituents are far too complex to be described here. They may involve chopping, grinding, pounding, or otherwise disintegrating your starting material; dissolving it in any number of solvents from alcohol to acetic acid; evaporating, filtering, extracting solids with ether or chloroform; decomposing residues by adding acids or exotic chemicals whose names are unknown outside laboratories; refiltering, concentrating, precipitating; washing solutions through alumina powder and analyzing the colored layers formed as they dry; measuring the amount of ultraviolet light that various substances absorb; plotting weight curves.

If you are lucky, you end up with pure crystals of whatever it is you're after. Then you analyze the crystals. How much carbon do they contain? How much nitrogen? How many other elements? The last stage is to work out the molecular structure of the substance, the order in which the atoms are arranged within its molecules. It is an intricate and time-consuming task—but the reward may just be a Nobel Prize.

Harold King did not win the Nobel Prize, but in 1935 he did become the first man to isolate a pure alkaloid from curare. His achievement is recognized today as a classical exercise in organic chemistry. Starting with twenty-five grams—not quite an ounce—of tube-curare from a museum specimen, he obtained just over a gram of a pure crystalline alkaloid which he called d-tubocurarine chloride, and which he showed was the active principle of the curare.

In normal circumstances, presented with the alkaloid, doctors should have been able to forge ahead with its trials, confident because of its purity that they could predict its action with accuracy and measure the precise doses needed to accomplish their purposes. But curare, ever since the days of the conquistadors, had been no normal substance. It clung to its secrets to the last—for neither the museum that supplied King's curare nor he himself knew which species of liana it came from. King was thus in the

115

unusual situation of having isolated an alkaloid from a starting material he could not identify. And since he could not identify his starting material, and was thus unable to get more of it, neither he nor anyone else could repeat his feat and produce *d*-tubocurarine in sufficient quantities for it to be tried out in practice.

This led to one last irony. When curare made its debut in the operating room it was as an extract of the raw jungle poison— even though Harold King had isolated the pure alkaloid and elucidated its chemical formula seven years earlier.

chapter

9

It was the worst possible news for this pale young man lying motionless in a bedroom in Washington, D.C. If he turned his head and looked through the window, he could see the trees in Rock Creek Park, their autumn-tinted leaves shimmering with sunlight on this breezy afternoon in October 1934. He had gazed longingly at those leaves during the past few days—for turning his head was the only movement he could still make. The rest of his long, lean body was frozen in a frightening paralysis.

Now he turned his head to look at the doctor who had just finished prodding and scratching him with pins and rapping his knees and elbows with a little rubber hammer—none of which he had been able to feel. Sadly the doctor confirmed his worst fears. There was nothing anyone could do. It was a puzzling case. There was no infection gnawing away at his body, nothing that could be treated with medicine. But somehow his nerves were degenerating and causing this rigid contraction of his muscles known as spastic paralysis. He could only rest, take plenty of vitamins, get as much sunlight as possible—and hope. One day, perhaps, he might walk again after a fashion, since patients with

117

similar symptoms often experienced periods of inexplicable improvement. But he could never expect to walk as he had before. Nor could he expect to regain full use of his hands.

For the man in that bed, Richard C. Gill, fate could have reserved no crueler blow. Proud, restless, imaginative, as much an individualist in his own way as Squire Waterton had been in his, Richard Gill had dedicated his life to travel and adventure. His proudest possession had been his independence. Now, almost before he had begun, it was all over. At the age of thirty-three, he was through, a helpless cripple for whatever natural span remained to him.

But then the doctor said something that gave Gill's life a sense of purpose that became an obsession. Gill, the doctor knew, had been in South America. So he had undoubtedly heard of that Indian arrow poison called curare—perhaps he had even seen it used. It inflicted a paralysis exactly opposite to the type Gill was suffering from: it relaxed the muscles instead of tightening them up. If only medical science had some drug like that, there might be hope for Gill and others like him. But curare was a deadly poison; there had never been enough of it around for anyone to fathom its mysteries; and it had never been standardized so that doctors could dole it out in safe doses.

Those few casual words inspired Richard Gill to pit his formidable determination against his paralyzed muscles, to force them, for month after agonizing month, to answer once again to his will. Learning to walk became for him a personal crusade—for in one of those coincidences the most trusting reader would hesitate to accept in a work of fiction, Gill had become fascinated by curare several years earlier. He had not only heard about it, he had seen it prepared by the Indian poison-makers—on his own land, beside the hand-hewn home he had built for himself in the wilderness of Ecuador. And what is more, by his own practice of the white man's medicine and the distribution of the beads and mirrors and pocket knives which were the currency of those parts, he had made friends with the Indian medicine men and learned something of their lore. If those other doctors, in their white coats and their shiny laboratories, needed curare to heal him and others like him, then he, Richard Gill, could and would get it for them.

So, four years after that conversation with his doctor in Washington, Gill walked back into the jungle—falteringly, and with the aid of a stick. He returned with the largest quantity of identifiable curare anyone had yet brought out to civilization and then, by his writing, speaking, pleading, and sheer persistence, he persuaded other men with widely varied talents and experience to preside over the final taming of the "flying death."

Richard Gill was born in 1901, one of two sons of a prosperous Washington physician. As a boy, he liked to get off alone into the countryside, hunting in the Shenandoah valley, canoeing, fishing, sailing—anything so long as it was outdoors and free of the restrictions of city life. By the time he embarked on his premedical studies at Cornell University he was tall and slim, with a finely sculptured face, large blue eyes and brown hair, a sensitive, serious young man—not at all the type to run away to sea.

Yet that is what Gill did, after two years at Cornell. He signed on a tramp steamer in New Orleans, jumped ship in Buenos Aires, and joined a whaler as a deckhand. After a year at the South Georgia whaling station in the Antarctic he returned to Cornell, his slim frame now filled out with muscle, though he remained lean throughout his life: even though he was almost six feet six inches tall, his waist never measured more than thirty-two inches and his weight never rose above two hundred pounds.

Gill had always wanted to write, and he now abandoned his medical studies and enrolled in an English course. He graduated with a B.A. in 1924 and became an English instructor at Lafayette College, in Easton, Pennsylvania. Still drawn to the outdoors, he spent happy vacations as a summer ranger at a remote station in Yellowstone National Park, where his duties included dressing the wounds of the many visitors who wouldn't believe those cuddly looking bears might bite, and the burns of their fellow innocents who wouldn't believe the geysers were hot. He entered the details of each case in a notebook with a streak of compulsive orderliness that was to show later in his field notes from the jungle. And he was pleased to find that his love of the wilderness was shared by his wife, Ruth, a slim, dark-haired music teacher from Presque Isle, in northern Maine, whom he had met on a blind date at Cornell.

Assured of his wife's support, Gill decided to give up the classroom, which he found no more conducive to writing than his medical studies. He took a job in the sales department of an

American rubber company and in 1927 went to Lima, Peru, with a territory that covered not only Peru but Bolivia and Ecuador. The term had not been coined then, but Gill was the antithesis of the "organization man." He found the routine of business no easier to take than the restraints of the academic world and his career as a salesman lasted only two years. But this was plenty long enough for him to be bitten by jungle fever.

Always a persuasive talker, he found a couple of friends who were willing to put up the money for a ranch which he would build and run, with the stated intention of growing tropical fruit, coffee, and castor beans. In reality, the prospect of being a plantation manager appealed to Gill no more than any of his previous occupations; what he really wanted was a permanent expeditionary base on the edge of the jungle from which he could trek into the unknown to live with and learn about the Indians. For eight months he and Ruth roamed central Ecuador by pack train, seeking a site for their *hacienda*. Eventually they bought a large tract of undeveloped land on the eastern slopes of the Andes, in the valley of the Río Pastaza, a river that tumbles southward, often through deep gorges, to the Marañón and thence into the Amazon.

Here, on the upper edge of the rain forest, about five thousand feet above sea level and two degrees south of the equator, the Gills set about building their home. The nearest track that could be even laughingly described as a road petered out nine miles from the ranch. It led from the tiny town of Baños, whose muddy plaza and white-walled houses clung to the base of a snow-capped volcano named Tungurahua, the Black Giant. Range after range of hills ran up from the valley floor and while bananas and papayas grew outside the *hacienda,* half an hour's climb took the new proprietors of this equatorial Eden into a quite different climate where potatoes flourished.

Years before, some unknown Ecuadorian had tried to clear part of the area for pasture. He had left behind a four-roomed shack built in what he imagined was the American style. Its roof had long ago fallen in, its timbers sagged alarmingly, and in one corner was Ruth Gill's stove—an ingenious structure of caked mud with iron bars set in it to form a grill.

Within a couple of years, using beautifully grained *canelo* wood cut and sawed on the ranch, Gill gave this tumble-down shack a creditable resemblance to a mansion. In keeping with his expansive tastes, it had seventeen rooms, an imported stove carried in on muleback, a bathroom with hot and cold water and even a tiled shower which he contrived to feed with water from a bamboo flume. A native craftsman was found who could fashion locally growing reeds into wicker furniture in imitation of pictures clipped from magazines; kapok purchased from passing Indians made a perfect stuffing for cushions. Ruth Gill built up a colorful collection of orchids; macaws squawked on the verandah rail and tame monkeys scampered in and out of the house; Gill even laid out a miniature golf course. The Río Negro, as he named his "dude ranch," eventually became so comfortable that he was able to supplement his income by entertaining various travelers who passed through the area: naturalists, explorers, prospectors, and even some sightseeing representatives of the diplomatic corps from faraway Quito.

By now Gill was cultivating coffee, cacao, and castor plants; corn, potatoes, carrots, lettuce, and other vegetables. But as always he was more interested in cultivating the Indians. He already spoke Spanish and he soon picked up some knowledge of the Indian language, Quechua. He turned a corner of his back porch into a makeshift clinic where he would pull teeth, stitch wounds, and hand out white man's medicine—though he considered the dispensing of medicine something of a two-way street.

His faith in the Indians' medicine stemmed from an accident to his wife soon after their arrival on the ranch. They were standing on top of an embankment watching their Indian workers below shaping logs for the house when Ruth somehow slipped over the edge and tumbled twenty-five feet down the steep slope. As Gill described it later, she banged her head on a log, knocking herself out, badly wrenched her knee, and picked up more than sixty splinters from the chopped-over ground. For the medical treatment it looked as if she would need, she faced a long and painful journey "outside" on a horse litter. But one of the cholo, or half-caste, carpenters offered to treat her in the native manner and, to spare her the uncomfortable jouncing over jungle trails, Gill agreed to let him try. The old man concocted a poultice from the tallow of a guinea pig, dried herbs, and a handful of fresh green leaves. It extracted even the most deeply embedded splinters—in Gill's words, "like magic"—and none of the wounds became infected. Then the rough-hewn practitioner massaged Ruth's knee with tallow, bound it up with another poultice—and what Gill had diagnosed as a "slipped ligament" was perfectly healed within a few days.

Credulous though Gill may have been in his admiration of these jungle therapeutics, the experience awakened his interest in the Indians' plant remedies and he began to study them seriously. Had he not become so convinced of their value he would not later have been such an effective catalyst in the development of curare. The real jungle began about four hours on horseback from Gill's *hacienda,* and as soon as he had the ranch running on its own momentum he made frequent trips "inside" to get to know the Indians and their materia medica. Writing about his experiences later, in a book called *White Water and Black Magic,* he said:

> The jungle dwellers, wiser in the potentialities of their environment than we are in ours, have built up and made full use of a practical, natural pharmacopoeia. The raw materials of this are gathered directly from the forests and are manufactured and used according to a ritual and tradition inseparable—in their minds—from the drugs themselves.
>
> Despite the fact that much of their therapy is founded on witchcraft and a general, calculated-to-impress-the-dumb-laity kind of hocus-pocus, much of it remains highly practicable and workable. Accordingly, I concentrated my work on learning as much as possible about this primitive drug procedure and—what was most necessary—the peeling off of the overlying veneer of mystery and plain mumbo-jumbo from the actual structure of pharmacal truth. After that it was necessary to correlate what we might call terminal findings in the field with methods for the possible application of those same findings in civilized life . . . in medicine, industry, even cosmetics.
>
> This particular kind of descriptive field work is known as ethnobotany and has to do with regional names, lore, and uses of plants as illustrative or typical of the customs of a people. Really my actual work goes the usual definition one better, for I am also interested in the final, civilized employment of the

122

primitive plant drugs. That's the hard part, the final bridging of the gap between the jungle and the laboratory. It takes time, patience, money; the very things which are the hardest to come by and keep.

Seeking the secrets of the Indians' witchcraft, Gill resorted to some schoolboyish demonstrations reminiscent of Squire Waterton. His flashlight was considered a miraculous device for capturing the rays of the sun by day and releasing them by night. He would sometimes impress his Indian friends by waving his hand at a running stream and making it fume like the heart of a volcano—by surreptitiously tossing into it a capsule of titanium chloride. Another classroom exercise in chemistry would turn a glass of water into first "blood" and then "milk."

Eventually he managed to gain the confidence of a jungle chieftain of mixed Indian blood, half Jivaro and half of a neighboring tribe. Through his influence, Gill became an honorary *brujo,* or witch doctor, an honor symbolized by the presentation of a fiber headdress interwoven with brilliantly colored macaw and toucan feathers. Thus initiated, he was able to watch the Indians preparing their curare, and so that he could study their daily life in detail he persuaded the chieftain and his nomadic band to camp on his land for a while. It was a happy time. Leaving his coffee plants to fend for themselves, he would disappear into the jungle every day, accompanying his adopted tribe on its hunts and sitting up late at night writing his notes on the preparation of curare.

In 1932, after three years of this idyllic but lonely life, Gill decided to take Ruth home to Maine for a vacation. A few days before they were to leave, as he was riding around his land on a final tour of inspection, his horse reared on a jungle trail. He was thrown sideways off his saddle and landed hard with both heels on a large flat rock. "I felt as if my backbone had been given a quick squeeze by a giant press, and for a few moments I felt shaken and dizzy and very sick," he wrote later. "That night, the queer, not-very-painful feeling of a tight belt—which wasn't there—around my diaphragm was something to which I paid little attention. It was only vaguely uncomfortable, and didn't last long. This happened a few times at night, and I always forgot about it with the day."

123

But a few days later, enjoying a farewell dinner with the American minister at the legation in Quito, he had difficulty holding his fork, dropped a cup of coffee, and fumbled awkwardly with his cigarette. Back in the United States, he would occasionally stumble over curbstones. His hand would shake when he signed his name. He would nick himself when he shaved.

And then, three months after his return, he woke up one morning and found the whole of his right side paralyzed. "It wasn't there," he wrote later. "It did not exist. I know no other way of putting it. A week later my left side went too. I was just a bodiless head on a pillow. For months on end I never knew where my body was, or even whether my legs were lying straight or bent, or my arms were crossed or at my sides."

When the illness struck, Ruth immediately took her husband home to his father's house in Washington. It was there that the doctor that Gill ever afterwards called "the Eminent Specialist" delivered his diagnosis. The specialist was Dr. Walter Freeman, a well-known neurologist who now lives at Sunnyvale, near San Francisco. He diagnosed Gill's complaint as multiple sclerosis, a progressive disease of the nerves which was incurable at that time and is still incurable now. Gill firmly refused to accept this diagnosis, then or later, preferring to attribute his paralysis to the fall from the horse. But Dr. Freeman attended him in his last illness, in 1958, and he confirmed by autopsy his original diagnosis.

No one knows what causes multiple sclerosis but it is one of the leading nerve disorders and more than a quarter of a million people suffer from it in the United States and Canada, with a further quarter million having closely related ailments. It usually attacks people in their prime, between the ages of twenty-five and forty, and its effect is to eat away the fatty covering called myelin which normally protects and insulates the nerve fibers of the spinal cord and brain, causing the blocking or garbling of signals from the brain to the rest of the body. The multiple scars, or sclera, formed where the nerve covering is damaged give the disease its name.

Early warning signs of its onset may include slurred speech, tingling sensations or numbness in various parts of the body, and poor coordination. In the later stages, the patient may be overcome by shaking and trembling he is powerless to control, extreme tingling sensations or numbness in various parts of the body, and weakness, and progressive paralysis of the muscles. About half of those who contract the disease become so incapacitated within ten years that they are unable to work.

Many theories have been advanced to explain how people get multiple sclerosis. Some unknown climatic factor may be involved, since the disease is common in colder climates and rare in the south. It may be caused by a virus, but if so all attempts to discover it have so far failed. It may result from a dietary deficiency or some change in the way the body uses food. Antibiotics, vitamins, various medicines, and many different types of diet have been tried as treatment, but at this writing none has proved successful. However, about eighty percent of multiple sclerosis victims experience unexplained "remissions," periods of months or even years during which the symptoms either disappear altogether or become much less marked.

This is what must have happened to Richard Gill, though his achievement in fighting back from almost complete paralysis to the leadership of a jungle expedition undoubtedly demonstrated near-fanatical strength of will. When Dr. Freeman mentioned curare to Gill, he was not advancing it as a cure for multiple sclerosis; he knew it could not be that. But he thought it might help to relieve the muscular spasms common to that disease, and several others, including the various forms of spastic paralysis in children caused by damage to the brain at birth, conditions now lumped together under the term "cerebral palsy."

It is not difficult to imagine the effect on Gill of this suggestion, tentative though it was. Here was a man of science, an eminent specialist, who appeared to share his own belief in the potential value to civilization of a substance born of the jungle sorcery that so fascinated him. Gill determined to win back the use of his body and go in search of curare.

He started by making desperate attempts to move just the tips of his fingers. Day after day he drove himself until he could wiggle a whole finger, or perhaps his big toes. Gradually, his sense of touch returned, until one day he found he could run his hands over the bedspread and tell with his eyes closed whether it was rough or smooth. He devised little exercises to help him. One of them was picking up marbles from one bowl and transferring them to another, using first his thumb and forefinger then his thumb and second finger, and so on. And when he had put all the marbles in the bowl with his right hand, he would take them out again with his left.

He was bedridden for the whole winter of 1934–35, unable even to feed himself. Learning to walk again was an interminable ordeal but he persevered, a few halting steps at a time, the sweat pouring from his face as he balanced on his crutches and forced his wasted muscles to respond to his will. It was two years before he regained enough mastery over his long legs even to drive a car.

But as soon as he could once again peck at his typewriter he started to write. He published a couple of children's books— adventure stories set in the Amazon jungles—and some more serious articles about curare and various native medicines in such publications as the journal of the American Museum of Natural History. And he never ceased to talk about and make plans for the expedition he was sure he would lead, though no one had any idea how he would finance it.

The answer to that problem came unexpectedly, in a letter from a rich Massachusetts businessman named Sayre Merrill. Fascinated by one of Gill's articles, Merrill sent him an invitation to visit him. Gill went—and returned with Merrill's promise of financial backing for his expedition. Now he began to prepare himself for his task.

He had no formal scientific training, but doctors, drug-company officials, and others who knew him have all spoken of his remarkable ability to absorb the most intricate technicalities of their specialized fields of knowledge. His method was to talk to those who knew their subjects, then complete his cramming course by reading the technical literature. "He was a genius, all right," a leading West Coast anesthesiologist who knew him in his later years told me.

In preparation for his expedition, he visited museums, doctors, drug companies—anyone who might conceivably be able to supply some kernel of knowledge he thought he lacked or who might be interested in the substances he intended to bring back. He discovered what quantities of the native drugs would be necessary for adequate chemical and pharmacological investigation of their properties; how to preserve them and pack them; how to collect the plants from which they were made and how to dry them and bring them back to civilization in a form botanists could identify.

And in May 1938, four years after the paralysis had struck, Ruth and Richard Gill sailed again for Ecuador. They planned to use the Río Negro as their starting base and were sad to find that during their long absence the jungle had crept back to reassert its domination over most of the land they had planted. A few days' hard work, however, restored the house to a somewhat bedraggled imitation of its former splendor and with the help of those of his employees who had remained on the ranch Gill began to organize the details of his trek "inside." He needed thirty mules to carry his two tons of equipment as far as four-footed beasts could penetrate into the jungle, and seventy Indian porters to take over from there. A messenger also had to be sent ahead to arrange for twelve dugout canoes to be waiting at the point where the party would have to take to the "white water."

Gill still could not walk without a stick and the three-week journey to the place where he had decided to establish his jungle headquarters must have tested even his considerable stamina. He was able to ride for the first three days, but for the rest of the way he had to limp along muddy jungle trails, slither through patches of bog, teeter across native suspension bridges that swayed alarmingly over rushing streams, and hoist his long frame painfully in and out of canoes. Going down one particularly steep, rock-strewn slope he passed a rope around his waist and gave its ends to two Indians who were then able to follow behind and slow his precipitate descent.

Arrived at his destination, he supervised the construction of six thatch-roofed bamboo buildings which included a field laboratory and a makeshift kitchen where Ruth Gill baked bread in an oven improvised from two empty gasoline cans. Then he spread the word among the Indians that he was interested in any jungle medicines they had to exchange for his needles and thread, fishhooks, matches, pocket knives, beads, and lengths of muslin. But he wanted to watch them prepare their medicines—and their curare—and collect samples of the plants they used, so there were frequent side trips into the jungle, some of them lasting days at a time.

Gill stayed in the jungle for almost five months, seeking out the plants used to make curare and evolving his own process for preparing it so that he could be sure it was uncontaminated by ant stings or other irrelevant ingredients dictated by jungle tradition. When he returned to the United States at the end of 1938 it was with dozens of crates containing not only twenty-five pounds of various kinds of curare but many other products of the Indian witch doctors. Each sample was neatly packed and numbered to correspond with the dried plant or plants from which it had been made.

Years later, when Gill died, his widow donated his field notebook and other papers to the Arthur E. Guedel Memorial Anesthesia Center in San Francisco. She also gave the center some of his jungle souvenirs which are preserved today in glass cases: his *brujo's* headdress, still as riotously colored as when the feathers were plucked from the birds to make it; a blowgun longer and thicker than the longest pool cue; gourds containing dried curare; a wooden quiver decorated with three bands of a simple geometric pattern and filled with blow darts, longer but not much thicker than toothpicks and looking deceptively fragile; bead necklaces and plaited tassels made from hundreds of iridescent beetle wings.

His field notebook, meticulously written up by Ruth Gill in their jungle camp, lists details of seventy-two separate plants he brought back: their native names, their descriptions, the locations in which they grow, the dates he collected them and the uses to which the Indians put them. Though the main purpose of his expedition had been to bring back curare, Gill spread his net wide and he had great hopes for some of the native remedies whose ingredients he had collected. He was confident that once these substances had been analyzed in the laboratory, valuable commercial products could be made from them—and by supplying the raw materials for them he would assure himself of a comfortable income and be able to live in style on the Río Negro, devoting himself to further study of Indian ways.

Had his luck matched his dedication, it might have worked. Gill had always been impressed by the Indians' glossy black hair and their freedom from dandruff or baldness. He found that they used a shampoo prepared by pounding the pinkish roots of a trailing vine to extract their juice. So into one packing case went a supply of these roots. Gill was convinced that this preparation—he christened it *Avelina rosada*—would banish dandruff, cure a whole range of scalp infections, prevent hair turning gray, and end baldness. In his files, there is a sworn statement by a New York graduate pharmacist who had been employed as a supervisor of cosmetic preparations for fifteen years. This man had been given some roots by Gill, had followed his instructions for compounding them, and had used the resultant oil on a patient whose head was "deeply encrusted with scale." Four applications of *Avelina rosada,* he said, completely cleared up the man's scalp, even though his condition had resisted ordinary dandruff removers for years. Another testimonial from a satisfied customer said he had "hair growing where none had grown before."

A proven hair restorer would no doubt have made Gill's fortune, but he could not persuade any cosmetic manufacturer to share his belief in its effectiveness. Even more far-reaching, had he ever been able to market it, would have been another native preparation whose secrets he was unable to discover until almost the end of his stay in the jungle—and then only with the help of Ruth. For this was a "woman-thing," a mystery beneath the notice of male Indians and too dangerous for any outsider to investigate: nothing less than an oral contraceptive.

Gill had noted the presence in every tribe of two or three unmarried women he euphemistically described as "bachelor girls of the forest" who, despite their promiscuity, never seemed to conceive children. He had also been told that no married woman in the area ever had to have more than ten children. He concluded that they must practice some primitive form of birth control. This, clearly, was an opportunity for his "chief cook and bottle-washer," as Ruth described herself, to make a more important contribution to the success of the Gill-Merrill expedition.

The Indian women were always fascinated by Ruth Gill, the first white woman most of them had ever seen. Untroubled by the ubiquitous jungle insects themselves, they could not at the beginning understand why a woman should dress in big boots and trousers like a man, but having spied on her through the bamboo screen as she took a shower they eventually accepted her as one of themselves. They seldom failed to watch with interest as she went about the camp's domestic chores, but it was many weeks before she could break through their shyness sufficiently to discuss such intimate concerns as their birth-control arrangements. Then they told her that when they did not want to have babies they took a medicine extracted from the root of a tree about thirty feet tall which they called tsecta.

Gill brought back a supply of tsecta roots and it is intriguing to speculate on what might have happened had he been able to overcome corporate skepticism and satisfy pharmacologists of their value. "The pill" just might have burst upon the United States before World War II. Ruth Gill remained convinced until her death in 1967 that those Indian women did have an effective method of birth control. But the drug companies—and probably the public as well—were not ready at that time to entertain such a revolutionary idea as an oral contraceptive.

Richard Gill was a persuasive man whose sometimes arrogant determination was softened by great personal charm and an aura of authority conferred partly by his physical presence and partly by his deliberate way of speaking, in a resonant voice whose power many an actor might have envied. Unhappily he was doomed to repeated disappointments in his efforts to "sell" the fruits of his collecting. One after the other, the products of the native pharmacopoeia for which he held such high hopes were tried and rejected, or rejected without any trial at all. For a time, even, it looked as though no one was interested in the curare which had been the *raison d'être* of his expedition.

As he hustled painfully from one New York office building to another, trying vainly to communicate his enthusiasm for his precious store of native pharmaceuticals to men who had seldom set foot outside a city, he must have felt that the business world was more of a jungle than the one he had only lately left behind in Ecuador. But the tragic, overriding disappointment of Gill's life, a disappointment that the most enthusiastic cooperation and support of doctors and drug companies could not have avoided, was that the vision which had inspired him to defy his disability and had sustained him throughout his search turned out to be illusory. Curare, even the refined and purified curare eventually made possible by Gill's persistence, proved no answer to the crippling muscular contractions of spastic paralysis.

chapter

10

One evening in the early 1930s, while Richard Gill was establishing himself on his far-off *hacienda,* a young New York orthopedic surgeon named Michael Burman went to the movies. Dr. Burman no longer remembers the title of the movie or the convolutions of its plot, except that in one episode the villain of the piece swiftly and mysteriously dispensed with an accomplice who was about to "squeal" to the police—by shooting him with a tiny blow-dart tipped with curare. Walking home after the show, Burman meditated on the strange properties of the ingenious murder weapon he had just seen employed. Like other doctors, he had encountered curare in the physiology lab during his student days. Suddenly it struck him that it might be the solution to a sad problem with which he had just been presented.

A friend had referred to Burman a little girl suffering from hemiplegia, or paralysis of one side of her body. The girl had already been taken to other doctors, and Burman was afraid he could do no more for her than they had. But what if curare, by relaxing her tightened muscles, should release her tense limbs and enable her to use them again? He resolved to make some inquiries about the drug and try it out.

A couple of years earlier, unknown to Burman, the same idea had occurred to an English doctor named Ranyard West, who was teaching pharmacology at Oxford University. West had found in 1930 that he could relieve tetanic convulsions in a dog with only half the dose of curare needed to produce paralysis. He transferred his experiments to human patients and by 1932 had treated thirty cases of spastic paralysis caused by chronic nervous disease. Sometimes the patient's rigid muscles were softened so that he could move limbs which had been immobile for years, but the effect always wore off within a short time and there was no lasting improvement. Furthermore, West encountered other problems, including sudden bronchial spasms, constrictions of the windpipe that cut off the patient's breathing. He persevered with his experiments for several years—but like all earlier investigators he was frustrated by the unpredictable effects of the only samples of the poison available to him and concluded there was little hope of curare ever being safely used in medicine.

Burman got his curare from the Merck Institute of Therapeutic Research in Rahway, New Jersey. It had been "standardized" by the only method then available. Its paralyzing activity had been tested in frogs; its effect on the blood pressure and breathing had been tested in cats; and the toxic dose for mice had been established by giving it to large numbers of white mice and averaging out the amount necessary to kill them. The company told Burman that working from this toxic dose he would have to determine for himself how much was required to treat a human being in safety. It also warned him that "since curare represents a mixture of drugs and in the future we may have to obtain new material which may come from different sources, you will understand that we cannot promise in advance that the subsequent supplies of the preparation will always be identical in pharmacological action."

It was hardly an encouraging beginning, but in 1934, at New York's famous Hospital for Joint Diseases, Burman began to use curare in an effort to treat those pathetic children whose limbs are twisted into grotesque deformities by spastic paralysis. Spastic conditions, in which the muscles are abnormally tight and stiff, form the largest category of the brain-centered diseases grouped today under the term "cerebral palsy." The most common cause of crippling in children, cerebral palsy afflicts perhaps six hundred thousand people in North America. Incurable, it is caused by damage to the brain before, during, or soon after birth, perhaps by the mother's catching German measles early in her pregnancy, or by premature delivery, or by prolonged labor—anything that interrupts the normal supply of oxygen to the baby's brain.

While the largest group of cerebral palsy sufferers are spastic, the disease may affect its victims in other ways. They may be "athetoid," meaning their head and limbs are in constant, uncontrollable motion; or "ataxic," meaning that they have poor balance. They may be able to walk, with floundering steps and flailing arms; or they may be bedridden and completely paralyzed.

Normal muscles receive intermittent impulses from the motor nerves even when at rest; they contract when the flow of these impulses is speeded up. In spastic children, the muscles are under a constant barrage of impulses. The area of the child's brain governing intelligence may be quite unaffected by the injury, but the constant rain of impulses from the damaged part holds his muscles in a continual state of tension.

Dr. Burman began by giving each new patient a tiny dose of the drug and working up to larger ones gradually. He always told the children they were "guinea pigs" and found they cooperated with him willingly. As soon as the child's eyelids began to droop he knew the paralyzing action of the drug was beginning to take effect and then he would slowly increase the dose until the locked limbs began to soften and relax—as the curare affected the myoneural junction and prevented the disordered stream of motor-nerve impulses from reaching the muscles.

The results were sometimes dramatic. Hands which had been quite useless might now be able to lift a glass of water or pick up a pencil and write. Occasionally a bedridden child might be able to stand, or even to walk, with some support.

Unhappily, the improvement was never permanent. As soon as the effect of the curare wore off, the paralysis returned. And throughout the four years during which he experimented with the drug, Burman, like other investigators, was plagued by its unpredictability. Both he and the chemists and pharmacologists at the Merck Institute had expected that the different crude curares might have varying actions. But in a paper describing his work in 1940 Burman pointed out that the so-called "standardized" preparations varied also. The drug did not always behave in human patients as it had behaved when tested on frogs and cats and mice.

This difficulty launched the Merck research staff on an intensive investigation of the properties of curare. In 1935 B. A. Krukoff, a botanist who is today one of the world's leading authorities on the curare plants, was sent to South America to collect the bark of various species of Strychnos lianas. Another botanical collector, Guillermo Klug, a German cavalry officer who emigrated to Peru after World War I, supplied Merck with samples of curare made by the Chazuta Indians of Peru. Krukoff identified the main ingredient of this curare as *Chondodendron tomentosum*—which, though no one realized it in those days, was to be the source of the curare used a few years later in the operating room.

All the material collected was closely studied in Merck's laboratories—though the paralyzing alkaloid still evaded detection—and when Richard Gill turned up one day and announced his intention of going into the jungle to search for curare Krukoff was asked to explain the intricacies of botanical collecting to him and supply him with the presses and other equipment he would need to bring back acceptable "vouchers," or botanical specimens.

But when Gill returned with his twenty-five pounds of curare at the end of 1938, he was dismayed to find that the Merck chemists had dropped their investigation of the curare lianas. Discouraged by the difficulty of procuring identified samples of the poison and effectively standardizing those available, they had switched their attention to an entirely different plant which was more readily available and also seemed to have a curare-like action, though it was not known to be an ingredient of any arrow poison. This was a legume, or pod-bearing plant, called erythrina. From the seeds of erythrina, Merck chemists isolated an alkaloid they named erythroidine. This has a paralyzing action, but it is less potent and more fleeting in its effects than curare and has never come into general use.

Krukoff examined the lianas from which Gill's curare had been prepared and identified *Chondodendron tomentosum* among

134

them. But while Gill fretted himself into a growing frenzy of impatience, the precious curare itself stood ignored in its unopened cans somewhere in the Merck laboratory. Weeks went by, during which he saw his hopes for his other jungle treasures collapsing one by one. It was unpleasant but at least he still had his curare. Surely that would be the triumph of his expedition. It must be—the future of so many pathetic cripples depended on it. Eventually, annoyed at Merck's seeming inactivity, he retrieved his cans and cast around for some more appreciative recipient.

He found one unexpectedly in May 1939, six months after his return from Ecuador. By this time, Gill had offered his curare to the drug firm of E. R. Squibb and Sons. He had had several meetings with Squibb executives during which he had given them the references he had compiled about the clinical work already done on curare and had tried to convince them of its potential value to medicine. He also stressed that the ingredients of *his* curare had been botanically identified. The executives seemed interested, and after the months of disenchantment his spirits were beginning to rise again—though he now realized that negotiations of this sort with big corporations took time.

Then one fateful morning Gill received a letter from Dr. A. E. Bennett, professor of neurology and psychiatry at the University of Nebraska College of Medicine in Omaha. He read it with an excitement he could barely control. Bennett had learned about his expedition from a friend, Dr. Walter Freeman—Gill's "eminent specialist." He wanted to know whether Gill could let him have some curare for experimental research into the treatment of children with spastic paralysis. And he added, cryptically: "I also have another idea in mind with reference to the use of this drug."

Gill replied immediately, agreeing to send Bennett curare on condition he was kept informed about the progress of the research. He had no inkling of what the "other idea" might be, but this midwestern professor promised to be a valuable ally in his negotiations with Squibb and his crusade to see curare introduced to medical practice. In a second letter a few days later, Bennett promised to furnish Gill with full reports on his results and added that a colleague at the university, Dr. A. R. McIntyre, chairman of the combined department of physiology and pharmacology,

135

had undertaken to do the work necessary to standardize the drug for use in human patients.

This association undoubtedly helped Gill in his dealings with Squibb, since the company knew and respected McIntyre's pharmacological work and had for some years been sending him new local anesthetics for testing. Two months later, Squibb contracted to buy Gill's curare and give it a full scientific investigation. At last the bow was being bent to speed the "venomous arrowes" toward their ultimate target.

Bennett never attempted to use curare in anesthesia—that was still one more inspired leap into an unknown future—but his "other idea" was to become the most important medical use of curare up to that time. And his collaboration with McIntyre, coupled with the faith and persistence of a few key men in the Squibb organization, set the stage for the last act in the drama.

A. E. Bennett was born in 1898 in Alliance, western Nebraska, a frontier town founded ten years earlier as the terminus of the Chicago, Burlington and Quincy railroad. Son of a fifty-dollars-a-month railroad conductor, he started work at the age of seven, peddling popcorn on trains. All through his school days he worked at odd jobs—cutting lawns, raising potatoes, laboring in sawmills and the harvest fields of the Great Plains, hawking aluminum pots and pans from door to door—and by the time he finished high school he had saved enough to see him through his first two years at the University of Nebraska. When this was exhausted, he dropped out and worked as a brakeman on his father's train for a year to earn money to complete his course.

After his graduation in 1921 he decided to specialize in internal medicine and, to finance his studies at the Philadelphia General Hospital, took a job as doctor in a coal-mining camp in Wyoming. In Philadelphia he served an eighteen-month internship at the old Philadelphia Orthopedic and Nervous Infirmary, where some of America's most celebrated doctors practiced, and the experience prompted him to abandon internal medicine for neurology. He studied for a while under the eminent psychiatrist Adolf Meyer at Johns Hopkins University in Baltimore and then returned to practice neurology and psychiatry in Omaha and teach at his alma mater.

Professor A. R. McIntyre, Bennett's colleague at Nebraska, is—like so many of those who figure in the curare story—a man of wide learning and unusual versatility. Born in London in 1902 of mixed Scots and English ancestry, McIntyre graduated from Manchester University as an engineer, but when the company he worked for failed he decided to study medicine. Invited to visit the United States by friends in 1925, he liked what he saw and stayed on. In 1930 he graduated from the University of Chicago with a Ph.D. in biochemistry, physiology, and pharmacology and won some notice with a paper on the working of the pituitary gland. A year later he qualified also as a doctor of medicine. After some further studies in Europe, he was invited to Nebraska and became chairman of the combined department of physiology and pharmacology in 1935.

When McIntyre received the first batch of Gill's curare he immediately set about standardizing it biologically so that Bennett could use it on human patients. Biological standardization does not guarantee that the finished product will contain a particular alkaloid or chemical, but that it will have a certain action, which may arise from a mixture of chemicals. It involves testing the material on animals and then diluting it to a uniform strength so that the doctor can judge how much of it must be injected into a patient to produce the effect he desires.

McIntyre's first task was to remove from the tar-like lump of raw curare the resins, gums, and other impurities that might have harmful effects on the heart or blood vessels. After dozens of experiments on frogs, mice, rats, rabbits, cats, and dogs, he came up with a substance which, when dissolved in water, produced curare's classical paralyzing effect in dogs without any apparent side-effects.

The patient Bennett chose for his first experiment was a nine-year-old boy—"as bad a case of spastic paralysis as you could possibly imagine." His arms were twisted rigidly in front of him, his fingers contorted and helpless; his matchstick legs were drawn up almost to his chest. Repeated attempts to relieve his paralysis by surgery had failed. So had attempts to straighten his arms and legs by encasing them in plaster casts: his overtense muscles tried so hard to pull his limbs back into their unnatural positions that he developed severe ulcers from the pressure of the casts. He was an intelligent and cooperative boy, but he could not even feed himself.

Bennett gave that first dose of curare very cautiously, but with

Burman's work to guide him he felt confident he would not run into trouble. As the drug took effect, it did what the surgery had not been able to do: the boy's locked limbs became limp and flaccid and Bennett was able to manipulate them into any position he chose. The paralysis returned as soon as the curare wore off, but he persevered with the treatments for eight months and believed they helped the boy to tolerate the casts he had been unable to wear before.

His next case was a twelve-year-old girl, her arms and legs paralyzed and her whole body shaken by athetoid movements. Bennett treated her for five months and found the curare produced a marked improvement which enabled the girl to reap more benefit from physiotherapy—so much so that she was eventually able to walk and feed herself, neither of which she had been able to do before.

The next case, however, was a disappointment—and the next, and the next. Soon he was forced to the same sad conclusion that Burman had drawn. His paper describing his experience is studded with phrases such as "only temporary improvement," "the curare effect was too transient and fleeting."

Bennett's first unfavorable reports on the value of the treatment were a bitter blow to Richard Gill. They also caused some concern to the Squibb company which, having taken over Gill's curare, continued to supply it to McIntyre and Bennett while its own research staff worked to standardize it in a form suitable for marketing. But marketing to whom, and for what purpose, if it was worthless in the treatment of spastic diseases?

Already, however, Bennett was elated at the apparent success of his "other idea." In October 1939 he wrote a letter to Dr. H. Sidney Newcomer, associate medical director of the Squibb company, which he began, borrowing a metaphor from outside his profession: "I think we have made a 10-strike in the use of curare."

In the late 1930s, there was introduced into the United States a revolutionary—and controversial—treatment for the most widespread and intractable mental illness facing psychiatrists: schizophrenia, or *dementia praecox,* in which the patient loses all contact with reality and retreats into a terrifying world of his own, haunted by all sorts of strange, private fears. He may become convinced his doctor is a spy plotting to poison him; he may

138

hear voices or see ghostly apparitions; if his disease takes the form of what is called "catatonia," he may alternate between wild rages and periods of impenetrable stupor in which he huddles in a corner, refusing to talk to anyone, to eat, to dress himself or even to move, periods during which he may stand for hours, staring with apparently unseeing eyes and perhaps holding an arm above his head in a posture a sane person could not maintain for minutes, let alone hours.

At least three million North Americans are treated every year for some form of mental disturbance, ranging from mild emotional troubles to incurable insanity. In the 1930s it had just been realized—and the news made headlines—that fully half of all the hospital beds in the United States were occupied by psychiatric patients. And about half of these patients were schizophrenics, who were only rarely helped by any form of treatment.

Then two European psychiatrists discovered almost simultaneously that some schizophrenics could be cured by drugs. Dr. Manfred Sakel, a young Viennese, gave his patients injections of insulin, which lowered their blood-sugar levels and deprived the brain of the glucose it needs to function properly, causing them to sink into comas. After several comas many of Sakel's patients made remarkable recoveries which neither he nor anyone else could explain. Occasionally a patient would go into frightening convulsions, but Sakel was always standing by ready to rescue them with injections of glucose.

Dr. Ladislaus von Meduna, a Hungarian, went one step further, deliberately provoking the convulsions with first camphor and then a drug derived from it, metrazol. The injection of metrazol into a vein would hurl his patients into violent contortions like those of an epileptic fit. But when the fit passed, they were frequently more lucid, able to take their place once again in the real world.

Though no one understands even today just how shock therapy works, it was the first successful treatment ever known for those unhappy souls who not so many years before had been chained to the walls of their cells. But metrazol treatments were justly feared by patients. They would lie in bed in an agony of apprehension as the nurses and orderlies needed to hold them down during their ordeal gathered in the room. Then the doctor would inject the drug into their arm—and in the forty-five seconds or so before they blacked out in their shattering convulsions they would suffer an uncontrollable sensation of panic as the drug overcame their brain. It was a traumatic experience for the doctors and nurses, as well as the patients.

Then a few years later two Italian doctors, Cerletti and Bini, discovered that these healing seizures could also be provoked by electric shocks, which knocked the patient out instantaneously, so that he had no memory of them afterwards. Electric-shock therapy proved just as effective as metrazol, much less frightening, and safer.

Bennett began to use metrazol soon after it was introduced to the United States—and he made an important discovery. He noticed that while many schizophrenics failed to benefit from shock treatment, it was almost completely successful in patients with the "affective psychoses"—those mental illnesses whose victims suffer severe, months-long fits of depression which often drive them to suicide.

"This has proved to be one of the most remarkable specific therapies of modern psychiatry," he wrote. "Ninety percent of severe resistant depressions . . . clear up within three or four weeks after six or eight convulsive shocks, either by metrazol or by electric-shock convulsions."

Ninety percent—nine out of ten patients—cured! It was an astonishing claim. If only five out of ten patients hitherto considered beyond help could thus be shocked into their senses—or three, or even one—why should this revolutionary treatment have been so controversial?

The answer is that shock treatment, whether by metrazol or electricity, had an unwanted side-effect so drastic that some doctors refused to consider its use, and others who were impressed by its apparent effectiveness were nevertheless convinced it would have to be abandoned.

When you raise a glass to your mouth, the muscles on the front of your upper arm receive a succession of impulses from the motor nerves which cause them to contract. To compensate for this, the muscles on the back of your upper arm relax and become longer, permitting your elbow to bend. In a willed movement, this always happens: the messages sent to contract one set of muscles are accompanied by messages telling the opposite set of muscles to relax.

Shock treatment produces something like a general uproar in the brain and the din spills over into the motor nerves. Hundreds of conflicting electrical impulses pour down the nerves, jolting opposing sets of muscles into action at the same time. These unco-ordinated impulses make the opposing muscles pull against each other, with enough force to tear the muscles themselves, dislocate joints, and even break bones.

Many efforts were made to prevent injury during shock treat-ments. Patients were bent backwards over sandbags, strapped into position, held by orderlies. But the uncoordinated muscular con-tractions still broke their bones and dislocated their joints. Some would incur fractures of their shoulders, or both hips. One doctor assembled statistics showing that from forty-three to fifty-one per-cent of patients undergoing shock treatment received compressive fractures of their spines which left them in pain for weeks or even months after the treatment.

"This is not real therapy," wrote one doctor. "Anything that actually injures the patient whom we are supposed to be looking after should be stopped." And shock treatment might well have been stopped—had it not been for A. E. Bennett's "other idea." The "10-strike" about which Bennett wrote to the Squibb com-pany in 1939 was his administration of curare to a patient about to undergo shock treatment with metrazol. The man was a chronic schizophrenic, a hopeless case who had been confined to the Lincoln State Hospital, near Omaha, for many years. He had no known relatives and was one of the true lost souls of psychi-atry, catatonic and so irrevocably withdrawn into his solitary, tortured world that he was more vegetable than man.

Bennett, with the benefit of Burman's experience, had not been unduly worried about giving curare to the spastic children. He had been able to begin with innocuous doses of the drug and increase them gradually, controlling the degree of muscular re-laxation he required and not taking the children anywhere near the point where their breathing might be affected. But what he proposed to do now was quite different. Metrazol convulsions were tricky things to handle. Once provoked, they had to run their course; there was nothing the doctor could do to arrest them. What complications would the addition of curare cause? Would the drugs react against each other in some dangerous way?

No one knew the answer to that question—and there was only

one way to find out. On the day chosen for the test Bennett entered the room where the patient lay in his perpetual mindless daze. He reached for the man's arm, found his vein and slowly injected McIntyre's solution of curare. He waited a few minutes for it to take effect, and then depressed the plunger of the hypodermic needle containing the metrazol. Now was the moment when the tormented man's body should have been catapulted into those horrifying convulsions. Instead, he lay still, only a slight twitching of his muscles showing that the metrazol was taking effect.

As later treatments showed, that first patient was too far advanced in his insanity for the metrazol treatment to benefit him. But at least it did not harm him—he had no broken bones or torn muscles. With one injection, Bennett had rescued a valuable form of medical treatment from possible oblivion. "It was quite a thrill to be able to do it and get away with it," he told me, recollecting that day twenty-seven years later.

It was also, as Bennett fully realizes, an experiment on a human being that would almost certainly not be countenanced today, with our more stringent regulations governing medical experimentation in both man and animals. "Quite frankly, it should have been done with monkeys first—but we didn't have the money for monkeys," Bennett says. "We had lots of guts in those days. We didn't hold back. I wouldn't have the courage to do it today."

Had modern regulations existed then, either the patient or his relatives would have had to sign a form sanctioning the experiment. The patient himself was obviously unfit to sign anything—and he had no relatives as far as anyone had been able to find out. The experiment might thus never have been performed.

To what extent is medical experimentation on living beings permissible? It has been a controversial question ever since the days of Claude Bernard, and public concern has led through the years to the introduction of various regulations intended for the protection of research animals as well as human patients. But what laymen consider praiseworthy humanitarianism sometimes seems to doctors to be merely an excess of emotionalism which could deprive mankind of valuable medical discoveries. Safeguards are essential, but in the last resort it is doubtful if they can ever be more effective than the doctor's conscience. At any rate, more than one doctor who helped to bring curare into medical practice has told me he might not have dared to conduct his experiments—even his experiments on animals—under present regulations. And the current U.S. requirement that research animals be anesthetized rules out certain experiments in which it is necessary to observe an animal's conscious reactions.

As it happened, there was another reason besides lack of money for Bennett to give that first injection to a human patient, rather than an animal. The addition of curare to metrazol therapy, for all anyone knew, might have destroyed its value as a treatment, since some doctors believed it was the convulsions produced by shock treatment that effected the cure, perhaps by liberating from the muscles some chemical with a healing effect on the brain.

Bennett's demonstration in his subsequent cases that curare did not lessen the effectiveness of the treatment was a valuable contribution to psychiatric knowledge, since it showed that it was the central effect of the shock upon the brain that was important, not the convulsions themselves.

Seven months after his first experiment Bennett was able to report that he had used curare in 101 patients receiving a total of 629 shock treatments. He had had only one spinal fracture, and that was in a patient whose veins were so poor that the effects of the curare had worn off by the time a vein had been located and the metrazol injected.

One fractured spine instead of the dozens that might have been expected! It was scarcely less remarkable than the initial success of the shock treatment itself. But curare was still such a sinister drug, and its dangers were so real, that many psychiatrists at first hesitated to risk using it. As late as 1948, nine years after his first successful case, Bennett published a paper designed to calm the fears of some doctors who still distrusted his method. Its value was eventually accepted, however, and when shock treatments are given today—to those patients who fail to respond to the major tranquilizing drugs introduced during the past fifteen years—they are always preceded by the injection of curare or a synthetic muscle-relaxing drug.

The collaboration between McIntyre, the pharmacologist, and Bennett, the psychiatrist, brought about the first truly successful medical use of the "flying death." It was a great achievement—even though it was destined to be overshadowed by the importance of curare to anesthesia—and it is sad to have to report that it led to a rift between the two men responsible for it.

Disputes over the origin of great ideas or discoveries are not confined to any one field of science, and the world of medicine has certainly had its share of them—witness the Morton-Jackson squabble over the introduction of anesthesia. They are always unpleasant and seldom resolved to everyone's satisfaction.

In 1947 McIntyre published a 214-page monograph on the history, botany, chemistry, pharmacology, and physiological effects of curare, which was greeted as a classic study of the subject. In it, he claimed that he himself had made the original suggestion that Bennett should try to cushion shock treatment with curare. This statement greatly offended Bennett, who still claims that the idea was his own. He also feels that McIntyre's book did not give him sufficient credit for initiating the whole curare project at Nebraska.

When Bennett wrote his original letter to Richard Gill, in which he spoke of having "another idea" for the use of curare besides the treatment of spastic children, he did not mention McIntyre. Neither did he two weeks earlier, when he wrote to the Eli Lilly drug company expressing his fear that shock treatment might have to be discarded because of the severity of the injuries it caused, and adding: "I have been wondering if we might not develop a drug that has a curare-like action that could be given prior to the convulsant to prevent these complications." Neither of these letters can be taken as conclusive, of course, since even if the suggestion had come from someone else he would not have had to say so.

It is unlikely now that the claim to priority can ever be proved. But when two men work as closely on a project as Bennett and McIntyre did, some cross-fertilization of ideas is only to be expected. In a letter to me in 1967, Professor McIntyre wrote from Nebraska: "My statement regarding my suggestion to A. E. Bennett is to the best of my belief the truth—and no doubt A. E. Bennett truthfully believes that the idea originated with him. Certainly we talked about curare together on many occasions . . . It is my wish that Dr. A. E. Bennett receives all due credit for his energy and enterprise in establishing the clinical use of curare—which, I am sure, led to its subsequent important role in anesthesia."

Whatever the merits of the dispute, whoever had the idea first, the collaboration was a success: McIntyre developed a usable preparation of curare and Bennett administered it successfully to patients. And their progress reports were eagerly awaited at the Squibb Institute for Medical Research at New Brunswick, New Jersey, where Gill's curare was still being analyzed in an attempt to develop a standardized, marketable product.

By this time Gill, once again embroiled in the business negotiations he always found so frustrating, had become disillusioned with Squibb. Having sold the company his original batch of curare, he now sought the exclusive right to continue supplying it. He hinted that only he knew the composition of the best curare for medical use, and tried to persuade the company to finance another expedition to Ecuador, during which he would supervise the collection of the right plants and their conversion into a pure curare, which he would then ship to Squibb.

The Squibb executives considered this an unjustifiable expense. They formed the impression Gill was trying to "corner the market" and pointed out that no one could monopolize a natural substance such as curare. Furthermore, since it now appeared that *Chondodendron tomentosum* was the plant with the curare action they were seeking, they felt Gill should ship them supplies of bark, which could be made into curare under controlled conditions in their laboratories. In that way, they could be sure of producing a product with a constant action, uncomplicated by snake venom or ant stings.

Squibb's hand was strengthened when it was able to buy a fairly large supply of curare from an explorer named August Rabaut, who specialized in bringing back rare fish from the Amazon. Rabaut was able to identify *Chondodendron tomentosum* botanically and he supplied the company with curare prepared from it on several occasions.

After this, Squibb signed an agreement with an American company called Astoria Pan-Americana, Inc., which had a botanist in Peru who was able to identify and ship the wood of the *Chondodendron tomentosum* plant the scientists at New Brunswick wanted. Some time later, though, Squibb realized Gill had been right in wanting to make the curare on the spot, since, when it was prepared from dried plants instead of fresh, it had much less potency. So Astoria returned to shipping the jungle-prepared curare.

All this was still in the future, however—the agreement with Astoria was not signed until 1941—when the Squibb scientists set about converting Gill's curare into a salable pharmaceutical product. That they succeeded was chiefly due to the vision and perseverance of the company's associate medical director, Sidney Newcomer, and to a highly successful method of testing its potency devised by Squibb's senior scientific staff member, Horace A. Holaday.

When Gill had approached Squibb in 1939, Newcomer was the first executive he met. As he poured out his hopes for curare, he could not have had a more receptive listener, for he found in Newcomer a man of exceptionally diverse talents and accomplishments who thrived on new ideas, a lifelong inventor who never lost his zest for scientific discovery. He first practiced as a pathologist, then turned to research into the electrical nature of nerve impulses and in the early 1920s went to Europe to study opthalmology. (At around the same time he took out twenty or so optical patents, including one for a wide-screen lens. Years later, when Hollywood turned to the wide screen to combat television's inroads on movie receipts, these patents were unearthed and he was retained as a consultant by 20th Century-Fox.) The depression frustrated Newcomer's attempts to establish himself as an opthalmologist in New York and once again he switched careers, joining Squibb in 1930 and turning his attention to the production and clinical investigation of new drugs. But he retained his interest in optics—so much so that during World War II, while still employed at Squibb, he set up a company to manufacture badly needed lenses for artillery rangefinders. And in 1968, at the age of eighty, while theoretically in "retirement," he was immersed in research to discover new applications for the laser beam.

A man with such broad interests and such a lively imagination could hardly fail to be intrigued by Gill and his curare. The Squibb management was more skeptical. Little was known about this strange jungle product except that it was a highly dangerous poison which appeared to be of no use to anyone except Indian hunters and physiologists. Why invest thousands of dollars in a research project designed to produce a drug for which there might

146

be no demand? Newcomer was convinced of curare's potential value, however, and his enthusiastic advocacy eventually won the day. The deal with Gill was closed and his carefully numbered cans were handed over to Horace Holaday.

A physiologist and pharmacologist, Holaday could have served as the prototype for a movie scientist. Tall and gaunt, he had dark, deep-set eyes behind thick-rimmed spectacles, bushy black eyebrows, and a neatly trimmed goatee. Modest and retiring, he was nevertheless a brilliant pharmacologist and an efficient administrator who stood high in the Squibb hierarchy. Holaday immediately began to study what little was known at that time about the composition of curare, and the conflicting and sometimes contradictory accounts of its action. When the reports from Nebraska came in, he read them with interest. But while McIntyre's method of standardizing the drug had enabled Bennett to use it on human patients, it was not, Holaday realized, accurate enough for the mass production of a salable product, constant in its action from batch to batch. One of McIntyre's tests involved the immersion of frog's muscle in a bath containing a solution of curare—a process similar to that used by Claude Bernard in his original researches. But Holaday found that some curare preparations standardized in this way, even from the same source, had widely differing activities when administered to human patients.

Toward the end of 1939, he solved the problem by evolving a potency test so precise that it is still regarded as a classical achievement in the realm of biological assay. The traditional way of testing a drug intended for human beings is to administer it to animals and carefully measure the quantity needed to kill them. By adjusting this figure mathematically, laboratory researchers can predict a safe dose for human beings. The trouble with this system is that because of the differences within animal species large numbers of animals must be sacrificed to arrive at the average fatal dose with certainty. For instance, testing each new batch of insulin produced for the control of diabetes used to demand as many as one thousand mice, a lot of people, and considerable time. Automated methods supplanted this test only recently.

Holaday discovered a method of assaying the strength of a purified curare solution without killing his test animals—rabbits.

The ears of rabbits are liberally laced with blood vessels and he found that by injecting a solution of curare into them at a carefully controlled rate a point was reached at which the rabbit's head slumped down between its paws and it was unable to lift it. If the flow of the solution was immediately cut off at that point, the rabbit recovered within a few minutes without ill effect. This enabled the same rabbit to be used for repeated tests and it turned out that the quantity of curare required to make its head drop was always the same. Thus if one cubic centimeter of the solution was established as one unit for control purposes, and it took only half a cubic centimeter of a new batch of the drug to bring down the rabbit's head, the new batch was twice as potent as the control sample. Knowing this, it was a simple matter to dilute it to uniform strength.

Holaday's rabbit head-drop test was far more reliable and accurate than any previous biological assay, and it is still used at New Brunswick today to standardize batches of the pure alkaloid d-tubocurarine for medical use. It is, in fact, unique: it is the only biological test that proved more precise than a chemical assay. This was discovered after two Squibb scientists, Drs. James Dutcher and Oskar Wintersteiner, became in 1942 the first investigators to isolate d-tubocurarine from a botanically identified specimen of *Chondodendron tomentosum*. Testing a batch of the supposedly pure alkaloid, the laboratory staff found their rabbits were being knocked out much sooner than they should have been. Further chemical analysis disclosed that the d-tubocurarine contained another substance with three times the potency but a much more transient effect.

In 1939, of course, when Holaday first began work on Gill's curare, no one knew what its active ingredient was. But samples tested in the rabbits were sent to Bennett and McIntyre for further trials. They proved so uniform and predictable in their action that Newcomer decided the solution should be made up in ampuls for distribution to other psychiatrists who, impressed by Bennett's results, were anxious to try curare for themselves. Holaday named the new drug Intocostrin and the ampuls began to go out to a few selected doctors early in 1940.

Intocostrin was the culmination of a long search, the first commercial preparation of curare which doctors could give to patients in measured doses to produce a predictable action, with no fear of undesirable side-effects. But no amount of refining and standardization, of course, can make curare a "safe" drug. If the dose given is large enough, there is always the danger of death from suffocation. This, and the general aura of dread which had clung to curare since the days of Peter Martyr, made the Squibb management reluctant to market Intocostrin.

As the months passed and more doctors approached him for experimental supplies, Newcomer became more convinced than ever of its value. He wanted to apply to the Food and Drug Administration for permission to put it on sale to doctors, but management forbade him to do so—perhaps fearful of public reaction to the sale of such a sinister substance, or perhaps apprehensive about the danger of accidents if its users did not exercise proper care.

As a concession to Newcomer's enthusiasm, Carleton Palmer, president of Squibb, agreed that he could continue to distribute ampuls of the drug to selected doctors wishing to experiment with it, as long as there was no cost to the company. So Newcomer distributed the drug at his own expense, charging $5 an ampul wherever he could and handing the money over to the Squibb treasurer.

By the end of 1941 he was able to report that several thousand shock treatments had been safely carried out with Intocostrin, including more than fifteen hundred by Bennett alone. Two deaths had occurred—but one had been shown to have no connection with the drug and the other was thought to have been caused by failure to apply artificial respiration when needed. Still the Squibb management hesitated. Eventually Newcomer went to see one of his friends, Dr. J. J. Durrett, who happened to be medical director of the FDA. After hearing his account of Intocostrin's preparation and the use that had been found for it, Durrett said he thought there would be no difficulty getting FDA approval for its sale. This initiative earned Newcomer a reprimand from the Squibb management but eventually an elaborate new-drug application was prepared and submitted. It consisted of five volumes of botanical, chemical, and pharmacological information about Intocostrin, together with more than five hundred clinical case reports. Altogether, the five volumes weighed nineteen pounds.

Most of those case reports dealt with Intocostrin's use in shock

149

therapy, which was considered its most important—if not its only—medical application. But at the time the application was filed, in April 1943, Intocostrin had already been at work in the operating room for more than a year. Newcomer, and Squibb, knew about this latest innovation, but it was still considered too "experimental" to carry any weight in a new-drug application. No one realized that in anesthesia, the sleep that blots out pain, the "flying death" had at last found its true destiny.

part

3

chapter

11

Pain, as we saw in the first part of this book, existed before the brain of man. Onerous though the burden may be at times, it is not one that we carry without purpose. Nor is it, as theologians once held, a divine punishment for our sins. Pain is our great protector, nature's first line of defense against injury to the animal body.

Very rarely, but often enough for some cases to have been documented in medical records, children are born without the capacity to feel pain. It is a dangerous handicap which, unless they are carefully and constantly supervised, can soon prove fatal. The normal child who puts his hand in a fire receives an unforgettable lesson that it is hot and should be avoided in future. Similarly, a single cut usually teaches a child respect for sharp knives. Deprived of the warning signal of pain, a child may unknowingly damage himself by bumping into sharp objects as he learns to crawl. Later in life he may ignore injuries as severe as broken bones simply because he doesn't feel them. One boy born without the sense of pain narrowly escaped death from peritonitis, a serious internal infection caused by a ruptured appendix he had not noticed, though a normal person would have collapsed in agony.

Pain is therefore essential to our survival. It is also one of the great mysteries of life, almost impossible to describe or to measure—and for these reasons to study with scientific detachment and exactitude. An injury considered trivial by one person can cause intense distress to another, because of their differing pain thresholds. And the pain threshold, the point beyond which an individual cannot stand pain, varies not only from person to person but in the same person at different times. One's capacity to bear pain may be lessened during a period of illness or anxiety, but quite the opposite may happen under the stress of fear or sudden shock, as when a painful injury passes unnoticed in the heat of a fight or an accident, making itself felt only later.

The age-old question of whether women can stand pain better than men will probably never be answered until men bear babies. And there are other curiosities of pain—the phenomenon of "referred" pain, for example, when an injury to one part of the body is felt in another part of the body entirely; and the phantom pains felt by amputees in an arm or leg they no longer possess.

"It's all in the mind" may be an oversimplification, but there is no doubt that man, with his superior brain development, is more susceptible to pain than lower animals. A creature without a brain, like the jellyfish, or with only a rudimentary brain, like the frog, responds to pain or any other stimulus only at the reflex level: a frog does not *think* before it leaps. But higher up the evolutionary scale, animal organisms become more "integrated," that is, the various parts of the body are more dependent on one another, more closely linked to, and dependent on, the brain.

Every boy who has ever been fishing knows that a worm cut in half continues to wriggle; its reflexes continue to operate. Some lower animals can even regrow limbs or tails torn off in battle. Man has a much more developed and highly centralized nervous system and an injury to one part of it thus has a much greater effect on the whole.

Interfering with a mechanism as complex and closely integrated as the human body, overcoming by anesthesia the sense of pain that is so vital to the body's welfare, is neither an easy thing to do nor one to be undertaken lightly. Doctors know *how* to do it, and as their skill has increased they have become able to do it with more precision and less and less disturbance to the proper functioning of other parts of the organism. But no one knows yet how anesthesia *works,* why certain substances have the power to circumvent a system designed by nature for our protection.

There are several ways of achieving anesthesia, and many different anesthetic agents, each with its own virtues—and disadvantages. The simplest technique, and the one that is easiest to understand, is that of local anesthesia. As we have already seen, pain is signaled by messages flashed along the sensory nerves. If these nerves could be cut, like telephone wires, the messages would not get through to the brain. But repairing cut nerves is a far more delicate and much less certain procedure than repairing cut telephone wires. What the anesthesiologist needs is only a temporary break in the circuit. And fortunately there are some chemicals which, when applied to the nerves, interrupt the electrochemical process by which their messages are conducted long enough for an operation to be performed without the patient feeling any pain.

For the first local anesthetic, medicine reached out to the jungles of the New World, as it had done earlier for quinine and was to do much later for curare. The conquistadors who looted Peru melted down the Incas' exquisite gold and silver jewelry and laid waste their magnificent aqueducts and architectural masterpieces —to the everlasting regret of succeeding generations of museum curators and archeologists. But fortunately they spared the country's trees. And they found that one of these, a small tree or shrub classified botanically many years later as *Erythroxylon coca,* was considered sacred. Various magical properties were ascribed to the leaves of the coca tree and chewing them was a divine experience reserved for the ruling class. The Indians made offerings of coca leaves to the sun and called their queen, whom they worshipped only slightly less than the sun, Mama Coca.

As the Inca empire disintegrated under the assault of the Spaniards, the leaves gradually lost their sacred associations and their use filtered down from the aristocratic Incas to their lowly subjects. Fortified by a wad of leaves chewed like tobacco, the Indians performed prodigious feats of strength and endurance on the slopes of the Andes, apparently immune to the need for food or

155

sleep. Many travelers commented on this strange property of the coca leaf and even experimented with it themselves. But it had to wait more than three centuries for any chemical investigation. Then, in 1860, a German student named Albert Niemann, working in a laboratory at Göttingen, isolated a heap of crystals from coca leaves; an alkaloid he christened cocaine.

Having tasted his crystals, Niemann reported that they "numbed the tongue." Once again, humanity was on the brink of a merciful discovery—and once again, no one realized it. It was twenty-four years later that a young Viennese physician named Sigmund Freud received a visit from a fellow doctor who had become addicted to morphine in his attempts to relieve the pain of a nerve tumor at the base of an amputated thumb. Knowing that cocaine had a powerful effect on the nervous system and believing, mistakenly, that it was not addictive, Freud administered it to his colleague and resolved to subject it to thorough study. But first he wanted to get away to Hamburg for a holiday with the fiancée he had not seen for two years. Had he not taken that holiday, the father of psychoanalysis might also be famous today as the father of local anesthesia. Instead, a colleague named Carl Koller, who specialized in diseases of the eye, took over his investigation of cocaine.

By 1884, general anesthesia had become universally accepted, but many eye operations still had to be performed without it. The eye is such a sensitive part of our bodies, and operations on it demand such delicate surgical precision, that it is almost impossible to conceive of their being accomplished without some form of anesthesia to prevent the involuntary blinkings and twitchings which must have complicated the surgeon's already difficult task. But absolute quiet and immobility afterwards are essential to the success of most eye operations—and after receiving ether patients were far from restful; they were only too likely to be racked by painful nausea and retching.

In fact, early anesthesia was such a dangerous and unpleasant ordeal that it was often reserved for only the most severe operations. This led to an ironical situation: while patients slept painlessly through major operations they suffered as much during minor ones as their grandfathers had before Morton.

Carl Koller had been searching for some substance which would make the eye insensitive to the surgeon's knife. He had

156

tried morphine, bromide, and other drugs, without success. Now he tried cocaine. He dissolved some of the alkaloid in water and dribbled a few drops of the solution into the eye of a frog. Then he touched the cornea with a pin. There was no reaction. He pricked the eye and scratched it—and still the frog did not blink or jerk its head away. Next he tried his cocaine solution on a guinea pig, and the results were just as encouraging. Finally, he used a human "guinea pig"—himself. It worked. However he probed his eye, he could not feel a thing. The cocaine completely deadened the nerves.

Koller's discovery, which was quickly taken up by eye surgeons throughout Europe and America, rested on the fact that cocaine can pass through the delicate mucous membranes which cover the eye and the inner surfaces of the body such as the nose and mouth, to reach and anesthetize the endings of the sensory nerves within the membranes. It cannot penetrate the skin, which is thicker and tougher than the mucous membranes, and so has no effect on the surface of the body. But it was not long before other doctors discovered that if they introduced cocaine *beneath* the skin, with a syringe and needle, it numbed any nerves with which it came into contact.

Inoculations and injections of all sorts are so common today it is a surprise to learn that the first crude hypodermic syringe was not produced until 1853. Nowadays anesthesiologists are equipped with syringes of several different sizes and hollow needles of varying lengths and thicknesses. Armed with these, and a considerable knowledge of anatomy, they can probe virtually anywhere they wish within the body, either just beneath the skin or deep into its interior, to surround a nerve with local anesthetic and interrupt its stream of messages to the brain.

Cocaine is no longer much used, since it was found to be more toxic than was desirable, whereupon chemists set about studying its molecular structure in the laboratory and attempting to rearrange it to overcome its disadvantages. Novocaine, the best-known and one of the first synthetic substitutes for cocaine, was developed in 1904. There are many others, with varying actions which anesthesiologists use for various purposes.

The chief advantage of local anesthesia is that it can be used for certain operations without subjecting the whole system to the disturbing effects of general anesthesia. And it is not, as might be thought, confined merely to minor operations. True, it will probably be used in a simple procedure such as the removal of a mole from a patient's face or back. In this case, using his finest needle, the doctor will first anesthetize a small area on the patient's skin near the mole. Then, passing a larger needle through this numb spot, he will probe back and forth under and around the mole, injecting a local anesthetic with each stroke, until he has isolated it behind a chemical barrier. All the nerves leading from the area to be cut must pass through this barrier and in the process their power to convey the pain of the knife is neutralized.

For a more serious operation, say the amputation of a foot, the doctor can employ a somewhat different form of local anesthesia. While an attacking army may be dispersed over a wide front, somewhere in the rear its communications must be concentrated in one spot. One well-aimed bomb on such a communications center may disorganize all the forward troops. Similarly, it is not necessary for the doctor to seek out and neutralize each individual nerve, if he can direct his attack on a communications center.

While the nerves of the leg are widely dispersed on its surface, they all come together on their journey to the brain, via the spinal cord. The main trunks into which they join are the femoral nerve and the great sciatic nerve. If these are "knocked out" by a local anesthetic, all the individual nerves below the knee will lose their capacity to transmit messages and the patient will feel no pain when his foot is cut off.

Even more vital communications centers are vulnerable to the probing needle of the skilled anesthesiologist. The sensory nerves from all over the body converge into the spinal cord and continue their journey to the brain protected by the spine. The spine would give them better protection if it were a solid bony tube, but in that case our ability to move would be severely restricted. So the spine is jointed. Its individual sections, the vertebrae, are cunningly overlapped, but it is still possible for the anesthesiologist's needle to be insinuated between the joints, where it can bathe the spinal cord itself with a local anesthetic.

How much of the body will be anesthetized depends on how high up the spine the anesthetic is permitted to rise. A local anesthetic near the base of the spine will remove sensation from both legs and the lower part of the trunk. Higher up, where more nerves from the trunk join the spinal cord, it will anesthetize both legs and the abdomen. Using spinal anesthesia, it is possible to abolish sensation from the whole body up to the neck and shoulders—though this is very rarely done.

The reason for this is that other nerves besides the sensory nerves are bound up together in the spinal cord, and a chemical that knocks out one set of nerves will also knock out the others. If a spinal anesthetic is used for an operation higher up the body than the abdomen, there is a danger that the motor nerves controlling breathing will be paralyzed and the patient may suffocate. There is also the danger that the "sympathetic" nervous system will be affected. This is the system that causes the muscles in the walls of the blood vessels to contract rhythmically and keep the blood flowing around the body. If it is put out of action the pressure falls and there is a danger of vital organs being starved of blood.

These handicaps apart, local anesthesia is such a neat and effective way of overcoming the pain of surgery that it might be wondered why general anesthesia is ever preferred. The answer is that there are several disadvantages inseparable from local anesthesia—among them the fact that its effects often do not remain "local." In the dosage necessary for the successful performance of a major operation, local anesthesia can have many undesirable side-effects.

Also, even though the anesthesiologist is careful to avoid the sensitive spinal cord—he injects his drugs into the cerebral-spinal fluid around it, rather than into the cord itself—there have been disastrous cases where chemical irritation has damaged the central nervous system, leaving the patient permanently paralyzed after the operation.

Some of the more complicated forms of local anesthesia take much longer to accomplish than general anesthesia and while they are being carried out it is much more difficult—and quite often impossible—for the anesthesiologist to control and support the patient's vital functions, such as breathing. Finally, undergoing an extensive operation under local anesthesia calls for a high degree of equanimity and cooperation on the part of the patient. Many patients, in fact, cannot stand the thought of remaining conscious and able to see and hear all that goes on in the operating room.

General anesthesia, in contrast, acts on the brain to produce complete unconsciousness. It numbs the nerves governing all the patient's senses, not merely his sense of feeling and perception of pain. He can no longer see, hear, or think. He neither knows nor cares where he is or what is happening to him.

But general anesthesia must not be allowed to overcome much more than these senses. The attack must be selective and the objective limited. For the nervous activity constantly going on in the body controls more than our five senses. Most of it is subconscious, directing the working of organs such as the stomach and intestines, the kidneys, liver, and heart. And if all this vital subconscious activity were suppressed the result would not be anesthesia but death.

That general anesthesia can blot out consciousness without arresting these vital subconscious functions is not due to the skill of anesthesiologists but to a fortuitous phenomenon of evolution. The brain, that supreme creation of nature, was built up infinitely slowly, layer upon layer, through millions of years. The stages of its building can be traced in the development of the embryo human brain. Life began in the sea, and a few weeks after conception the brain of an embryo human has many resemblances to that of a fish; later, it can hardly be distinguished from that of an ape.

Long before man became man, it was necessary for his forebears to develop hearts to pump the blood around their bodies and, as they left the ocean for the land, lungs to breathe the air. The centers that control those functions were thus laid down early in the development of the brain, and they remain at the base of our brains today. The faculties we developed much later, the faculties of thought and memory and speech, are controlled from the higher layers of the brain, the last ones to be laid on the top of this miraculous structure. And these latest additions to the brain are the most delicate; anesthesia knocks them out long before it penetrates to the lower levels where the more vital functions are deeply embedded.

This happy accident enables a general anesthetic, properly administered, to overcome the patient's sense of awareness of himself and his surroundings, including his perception of pain, without causing too much interference with such processes as breathing and the rhythm of the heart. But to act on the brain, the anesthetic must first reach the brain. The anesthesiologist cannot go probing into the brain with his hypodermic needles in the same way as he attacks the nerves in local anesthesia. To invade the bony citadel of the skull he needs an accomplice on the inside. And so he makes an ally of the blood.

Each of the fourteen billion cells in the brain needs a constant supply of oxygen, glucose, and other nutrients. These essential "foods"—deprived of them for a mere few minutes the cells will die—are spread through the brain by the blood, flowing through an intricate network of blood vessels, most of them too fine to be seen without a microscope and many of them only wide enough for one red blood corpuscle to squeeze through at a time. If a drug can be dissolved in the blood, it too will be distributed among the brain cells. It will also, since the blood circulates all round the body, be carried to every other organ and tissue, and this can be a handicap, as will be seen later.

The simplest method of introducing a drug into the blood is to inject it into a vein. (Arteries are not used, for a variety of reasons, among them the fact that they are far more sensitive to the injection of irritant substances than veins and can quite easily become blocked by them. This can cut off the blood supply to the part of the body they serve, even to the extent of causing gangrene and subsequent amputation of a limb.) To be injected into a vein, a drug must be in liquid form and diluted to a concentration that will not injure or irritate the tissues. The best-known example of this type of drug is probably the barbiturate thiopentone (better known under one of its trade names, Pentothal), which floats patients swiftly and comfortably off into unconsciousness. This is the drug the anesthesiologist injects into your arm as he asks you to count to ten. Long before you have reached that number you are asleep, and when you wake up the operation is over.

It will not, however, have been carried out under the influence of thiopentone, because unfortunately the drugs which can be injected intravenously are not satisfactory general anesthetics. They are unrivaled for the induction of anesthesia—for putting you "under"—but if given in doses large enough to keep you under while the surgeon carries out his task they may dangerously interfere with your breathing and the working of your heart, or leave you drugged and insensible for hours after the operation. So after you have been whisked into oblivion by the needle in the arm, the anesthesiologist must give you something else to keep you there when the cutting begins.

The agents he uses for this purpose are either gases, such as nitrous oxide or cyclopropane, or vapors given off by volatile liquids such as ether and the more recent halothane (known by the trade name Fluothane), which was introduced about ten years ago. Gases cannot be introduced into the blood by hypodermic needles because of the danger that bubbles may cause a fatal block in the circulation, much as an airlock will block the pipes of your heating system. But here again, nature comes to the anesthesiologist's aid.

The oxygen needed by the brain and the rest of the body is picked up by the blood on its journey through the lungs. But the blood is remarkably obliging about picking up hitch-hikers— sometimes dangerously so: if you run your car in a closed garage and thus offer your blood the choice between oxygen and poisonous carbon monoxide fumes, it will absorb three hundred times as much carbon monoxide as oxygen, to your eternal detriment.

In the same way, if an anesthetic vapor or gas is introduced into your lungs, it will be picked up by the blood and carried to your brain. This was the method—it is called inhalation anesthesia—used by William Morton. It worked then, and it still works today, though the technique by which the anesthetic is administered is now more refined and sophisticated. Morton's patient breathed ordinary air which picked up ether vapor simply by passing through a glass inhaler containing the liquid ether. Nowadays the anesthesiologist has a machine with tanks of anesthetic agents and oxygen under pressure, and taps and gauges which enable him to administer them in the correct proportions, thus ensuring that the patient always receives an adequate supply of oxygen. Between the taps and the mask or tube through which the patient breathes there is a "rebreathing bag," a rubber bladder which forms a reservoir for the mixture of anesthetic and oxygen. The rhythmic movements of this bag show the patient's breathing and it is a simple matter for the anesthesiologist to assist or even control his breathing by squeezing the bag in his hand. (There are machines which take over this function completely in the more complicated operations.)

Thus, carefully governing the concentration of the anesthetic and relying on his "inside man," the blood, to transport it to your brain, the anesthesiologist is able to cut off the reception of impulses from your sensory nerves and blot out all sensation of

162

pain even if an operation lasts many hours. But the banishment of pain is only one part of the anesthesiologist's job. Most of the muscles of the body, particularly the powerful muscles of the chest and abdomen, are in a constant state of "tone," or tension, even when we are asleep. Otherwise, our body would flop around with all the distressing anatomical disarray of a dilapidated golliwog. But taut muscles, while they help us to keep our shape, hinder the surgeon. If you cut a taut wire, its ends snap back dangerously. It is the same with a patient's muscles: before the surgeon can cut through them, or move them aside to work on organs hidden beneath them, they must be loose and flexible, completely limp and relaxed.

This imposes a double duty on the anesthesiologist. It is not enough for him merely to block the sensory-nerve impulses which register pain; he must also find some way of preventing the motor-nerve impulses from reaching the muscles and holding them taut and unyielding. Fortunately, the same anesthetic agents which knock out the sensory part of the brain and free the patient from the pangs of pain will also knock out the motor part and prevent it from transmitting the stream of messages that contract the muscles.

It seems like a neat and simple arrangement. But it has one grave disadvantage. For some reason, motor nerves are not so easily overcome by anesthetics as sensory nerves; they resist chemical interference with their functions much more stoutly. While quite a small dose of an anesthetic will render a patient insensible to pain, it takes a much heavier dose to relax his muscles sufficiently to permit the surgeon to work without hindrance. If anesthetics were completely harmless, this would not be a problem. But they are all poisonous to some degree. And if the anesthesiologist has to increase the amount of poison reaching the brain he has to increase its concentration in the blood—which in turn increases the quantity of poison carried by the blood to every organ and tissue in the body.

The type of poisoning, and the amount of damage inflicted on the patient, depend on the anesthetic agent used. Nitrous oxide is the safest and least harmful anesthetic known, but it does not relax the muscles sufficiently for operations within the abdomen or chest unless given in such heavy concentrations that the patient is starved of oxygen and in danger of suffocation.

163

Ether, in contrast, gives the surgeon all the muscular relaxation he needs—but only when administered in quantities sufficient to put the patient into a deep level of anesthesia, at the cost of such undesirable repercussions as depression of the action of the heart, the poisoning of body tissues with acid, and thickening of the blood caused by loss of essential body fluids. In addition, ether vapor is highly irritating and when given in quantities sufficient to relax the muscles it causes acute nausea and vomiting for several hours after the operation.

For many years, this unavoidable poisoning of the patient's whole system made anesthesia a hazardous as well as an unpleasant experience. Every surgical ward had its quota of patients recovering from operations, moaning under the double burden of blinding headaches and fits of painful retching and vomiting which threatened to tear apart their sutured wounds. Doctors watched anxiously for days after the operation for signs of pneumonia, since coughing was so painful that patients hesitated to risk it and their bronchial tubes became congested with mucus, making their lungs more susceptible to infection.

Pneumonia, before the days of antibiotics, could not be treated effectively. Many patients, particularly the old, survived their operations only to die from it. Countless others were prevented from having operations because their doctors considered them too sick or too weak to survive not the manipulations of the surgeon but the rigors of the anesthetic. Occasionally, patients laid on the operating table found the shock to their systems too much to bear. For them, anesthesia became a journey toward death from which they never returned.

There seemed to be no way around the problem. The surgeon could not do his job properly unless the patient's muscles were relaxed. But the patient's muscles could not be relaxed without an unwelcome trespassing on the healthy working of the rest of his body.

This poisoning of the patient's system, which barred the way to further progress in anesthesia, was called general intoxication. The word *intoxication,* as we have seen, was born of the ancient Greeks' unhappy experiences with poisoned arrows. By a curious coincidence, the general intoxication inflicted on patients in the operating room was to be banished by the most sinister arrow poison of them all.

chapter

12

There were many distractions—and attractions—for the 12,864 delegates attending the 91st annual session of the American Medical Association in New York City in June 1940. A week earlier, the last British soldier had been evacuated from the beach at Dunkirk. The United States had not yet entered the war, but some of the doctors at the convention had already become involved in the organization of the base hospitals being set up across the country as a preparedness measure. The sessions of the convention were held at the Waldorf Astoria, where a single room could still be rented for six dollars a night. For forty cents a delegate who wanted to get away from it all could watch Buster Crabbe and Eleanor Holm disporting themselves in Billy Rose's Aquacade at the World's Fair, out at Flushing Meadows. If he preferred Broadway musicals, $2.75 would buy him the best seat in the 46th Street Theatre, where Ethel Merman, co-starring with Bert Lahr, was belting out Cole Porter songs in *Du Barry Was a Lady*. And if he wanted to sneak away to the movies, he could see William Holden in *Our Town* or Laurence Olivier in *Rebecca*.

Not all the delegates realized it, but a far more dramatic film than either of these was playing in town that week—among the convention's two hundred scientific and technical exhibits, which took up three floors of the old Grand Central Palace. It was an amateurish production, with none of the typical Hollywood glitter, no big-name stars, not even a sound track. It showed a mental patient being given metrazol shock therapy, and it was not a pretty picture. The man's arms and legs thrashed wildly in the air, his back arched until it seemed it must break, and his whole body shuddered with the violence of the drug's assault on his tormented brain. In the next scene the same patient was given a preliminary injection of this fascinating new drug called Intocostrin; this time, when the metrazol was injected into his arm, he lay still, only a mild trembling showing that it was taking effect.

It was a convincing demonstration of curare's value in shock treatment, and the film won an A.M.A. certificate of merit for its makers—A. E. Bennett and A. R. McIntyre. But much more important was the profound impression it made on one of the doctors who saw it, a Squibb representative named Lewis H. Wright.

Curare was no new phenomenon to Lew Wright; in fact, years earlier it had helped him pay his way through medical school. As an instructor in the physiology department of Texas A & M, one of his tasks was to prepare the curare which was injected into frogs to teach medical students the interrelationship between nerves and muscles. In those days, during World War I, drug companies were not marketing curare as such; the university bought a supply of roots and bark alleged to contain the drug and Wright ground them up in a mortar, boiled the resultant pulp in water, and filtered the solution to obtain a yellowish extract which might or might not paralyze a frog. If it did not work, he got himself some more sticks and tried again.

After his graduation, Wright practiced as an obstetrician, but the experiments he had conducted with animals as a physiology instructor had given him more than the average young doctor's familiarity with anesthetics, a branch of medicine in which more and more physicians were beginning to specialize. In 1930 he gave up his obstetrical practice and joined the Squibb company as a representative specializing in anesthesia. And in 1940, when he saw the movie produced by Bennett and McIntyre, he suddenly realized what a boon curare could be to anesthesiologists.

Years ago, he had marveled at the way the juice he extracted from those South American twigs had paralyzed his experimental frogs and left them unable to twitch a muscle. Now he saw Intocostrin, a product developed by his own company, doing the same thing to human beings, without any apparent danger. If curare relaxed muscles so effectively, why use anesthetics to do the job? Why saturate a patient with ether or other substances and poison his whole system? If the muscular relaxation surgeons needed could be produced by curare, the anesthetic would merely have to abolish pain, and it could thus be given in much lighter, less harmful doses. General intoxication would be a thing of the past.

It was a simple idea, as revolutionary ideas often are. And as so often happens when a man conceives a revolutionary idea, others rejected it out of hand. No longer in practice, Wright had no opportunity to experiment with curare himself. But he was so excited at its possibilities that he immediately began trying to persuade others to do so. Before the A.M.A. convention was over he had mentioned his idea to several leading anesthesiologists and offered them experimental supplies of Intocostrin. They refused to take him seriously—and some even laughed outright when he broached the subject.

After all, everyone knew curare paralyzed respiration. Nowadays, anesthesiologists take over the functions of a patient's lungs during an operation without a qualm, but at that time if a patient stopped breathing on the operating table he was considered close to death and it was a frightening experience for the anesthesiologist, the emergency he most dreaded. In vain, Wright pointed out that Bennett had used the drug safely. The anesthesiologists countered that he must obviously have been using such small doses that his patients' breathing was not affected. Curare, all agreed, was far too dangerous a poison to be given in the doses necessary to relax the muscles sufficiently for abdominal surgery. The breathing of patients laid on the operating table was already likely to be depressed to some extent by the anesthetic; to supplement the anesthetic with a poison known to paralyze the breathing would be tantamount to murder. Doctors simply could not justify such a risk.

167

Wright refused to be discouraged by these doubts. He was convinced that if Bennett, a neurologist and psychiatrist, could use curare safely then anesthesiologists, who were supposed to know more about the physiology of breathing and the management of artificial respiration than other doctors, should be able to use it too. He continued to tell all the anesthesiologists he met about his idea and lectured them endlessly and enthusiastically on the merits of Intocostrin—its purity and predictability and its freedom from undesirable side-effects.

Eventually, his persistence seemed to be rewarded. Two well-known and respected anesthesiologists, Dr. Emery A. Rovenstine and Dr. Stuart C. Cullen, agreed independently to take some ampuls of Intocostrin and try them out. Emery Rovenstine was one of the most important figures in anesthesia in the United States between the wars and many of today's leading practitioners of the art studied under him. At this time, he was working in New York, and he handed over the Intocostrin to one of his research assistants, Dr. E. M. Papper, now chairman of the department of anesthesia at New York's Columbia University.

Papper began his experiments by injecting the curare into cats in the physiological laboratory at New York University's school of medicine. As he expected, the cats developed severe difficulty in breathing and some of them died in attacks strongly resembling asthma. But having arrived at what he considered a safe dosage level, Papper went on to inject Intocostrin into the veins of two patients undergoing surgery at Bellevue Hospital.

He was horrified at the results. Both patients stopped breathing and in his own words, Papper was "up half the night giving them artificial respiration." His report to Rovenstine was categorical: curare was far too dangerous to be used as Wright suggested.

Stuart Cullen's experience was no more promising. A quiet, businesslike man with a square, lean face and graying hair, Cullen is today dean of the school of medicine at the huge University of California. He has made many contributions to the progress of anesthesia but the one of which he is most proud is the fact that dozens of his former students hold faculty appointments on the staffs of U.S. universities, and no fewer than eight of them are chairmen of university departments of anesthesia.

When Lew Wright gave him some of his precious ampuls of Intocostrin, Cullen was professor of anesthesia at the State University of Iowa, in Iowa City. Every Wednesday afternoon he used to drop his teaching and administrative duties and disappear into the laboratory to do research into various aspects of anesthesia. On several of these Wednesday afternoons, he injected Intocostrin into the forelegs of dogs and watched carefully for their reactions. The dogs all collapsed within seconds, jerking spasmodically with their efforts to breathe; some of them nearly died. Their plight so alarmed Cullen that he never dared to take the next step and administer curare to a human patient. His report to Wright, like the one Papper prepared for Rovenstine, ruled out the possibility of ever introducing Intocostrin to anesthesia.

Wright's hopes seemed doomed. Curare had a bad name and it looked as though its sinister heritage would bar it from the operating room forever. And yet had Cullen and Papper and Rovenstine and all the others only known it, Lew Wright's idea was not only practicable, it had been done before—almost thirty years before!

Medical history is full of examples of discoveries being made before their time—that is, before the world was ready for them, either because they gave so great an offense to the prevailing weight of orthodox opinion that their validity simply could not be acknowledged, or because the general body of associated knowledge needed to support and exploit them did not yet exist. In the field of discovery, the times and the man must coincide.

Thus the ancient Philistines and Phoenicians blamed gnats and other insects for ill health, and Marcus Terentius Varro, one of Julius Caesar's doctors, wrote: "Small creatures, invisible to the eye, fill the atmosphere, and breathed through the nose cause dangerous diseases." Varro was right, of course, but he had to await the invention of the microscope centuries later for his justification.

And four thousand years before Harvey's discoveries on circulation of the blood, an ancient Chinese medical work stated: "All the blood of the body is under the control of the heart and flows in a continuous circle and never stops."

The Talmud, that voluminous collection of Jewish laws compiled during the first few centuries after Christ, counseled surgeons not to permit their hands to touch their patient's wounds, since "the hand causes inflammation." It was wise advice, but the problem of infection was conquered only by the independent labors of Pasteur and Lister in the nineteenth century—and sterile rubber gloves were an even later innovation.

Similarly, the world was not yet ready and the times were not yet right when curare was first used in anesthesia. In 1912 the pharmacologist Rudolf Boehm (whose ingenious classification system for curare was mentioned in Chapter Eight) gave a German surgeon named Arthur Läwen a supply of curarine he had extracted from "calabash" curare. Läwen injected it into several of his patients and found it enabled him to perform abdominal operations with only a light level of anesthesia—exactly what Lew Wright was vainly insisting it would do thirty years later.

Even had other doctors recognized the value of Läwen's discovery, they could not at that time have taken advantage of it. For one thing, curarine was not a pure alkaloid and its effects could not be predicted with the necessary accuracy; if others had tried to repeat Läwen's experiment they might well have experienced quite different results. Furthermore the whole associated body of knowledge that makes modern anesthesia possible, particularly the understanding of how to assist and safely control breathing, did not exist in Läwen's day and so if others had been tempted to follow his lead many patients would undoubtedly have suffocated to death. At any rate, Läwen was unable to find a regular supply of curarine and he seems not to have pursued his work any further. He did describe it in a paper but it attracted little attention. It was, in fact, completely forgotten until it was rediscovered by a British doctor named Scurr in 1951— by which time curare was being used in operating rooms all over North America and Europe.

Läwen was unfortunate that his discovery had no practical results, but his experience does raise the question of who should be given credit for the introduction of curare to anesthesia. Important inventions or innovations in any branch of science are seldom the unaided work of one man; the soil from which they spring has usually been well fertilized by the intellectual labors of generations of workers in the field. Years ago, this question was considered by Sir William Osler, the renowned Canadian physician and medical writer who taught at three great medical schools in three different countries: McGill University in Montreal, Johns Hopkins in Baltimore, and Oxford University in England. "In science," Osler wrote, "the credit goes to the man who convinces the world, not to the man to whom the idea first occurs."

It took a long time to convince the world that curare could be anything more than a laboratory curiosity, and the task was accomplished only by the efforts of many different men, working at different times in history and in many different places. But by Osler's standard—and it is generally accepted as the only possible standard—the credit for the final taming of the "flying death" goes to Harold Griffith, the Canadian anesthesiologist who defied both the fears of more eminent colleagues such as Cullen and curare's malign reputation, and in so doing revolutionized the practice of the medical specialty to which he devoted his life.

Harold Griffith had no formal training in scientific research and he was past fifty before he received his first university appointment. Much of his long career was spent at the bedsides of the men, women, and children who came to him in his busy practice as a family doctor. He did not give his full time to anesthesia until after he had become famous for his introduction of curare to the operating room.

Griffith's "secret," if great men must have a secret, was that he never allowed the sometimes dreary routine of general practice to blunt his enthusiasm and his intellectual adventurousness, his desire to learn more about his chosen field. Any innovator must have a strong streak of curiosity, and Griffith constantly sought out and tried new methods of treatment. He had a simple test for any new medical development: "Does it meet a real need?" His ability to recognize those innovations that did "meet a real need" was almost psychic, and once convinced that they would contribute to the safety or comfort of his patients he would strive to develop them, undeterred by the misgivings or inertia of more conservative colleagues.

Even in his seventies, when he was still at work in the operating room by eight every morning, he was admired by much younger colleagues for the clarity of his judgment, which enabled him to cut easily through the welter of irrelevancies sometimes found in medical papers and extract whatever seemed of value. His introduction of curare to the operating room was no rash experiment. It stemmed from knowledge and confidence painstakingly accumulated during his years of practical experience.

Harold Griffith inherited both his love of medicine and the faculty of thinking for himself from his father, Alexander Griffith, a physician who practiced homeopathy, a fact which was to have several interesting repercussions on his son's later career. An intricate and demanding form of medicine, homeopathy has been almost, though not quite, supplanted by twentieth-century developments in medical science. Though little known in North America, it is widely practiced in France and homeopathic treatment is available under Britain's National Health Service, presumably because homeopaths must take an orthodox medical degree before specializing. (Sir John Weir, one of the doctors to Britain's royal family between the wars, was a homeopath, and King George VI, who believed in homeopathy, called one of his racehorses Hypericum after a homeopathic remedy.)

The principles of homeopathy might bear re-examination by orthodox medicine, in view of the present unhappy incidence of drug-induced illnesses and such disastrous episodes as the thalidomide tragedy. Homeopaths believe that "like cures like," that illnesses can be cured by natural substances which produce the same effects on the patient's body as those produced by the illness itself. This belief grew out of the observation by Samuel Hahnemann, the German doctor who founded homeopathy in 1796, that quinine, which cures malaria, will produce the symptoms of malaria if given to a healthy person. The parallel with vaccination, which stimulates the body's natural defenses against disease, is obvious.

The trouble is that homeopathy also teaches that each illness in each patient is somehow unique. The homeopath must make a meticulous and time-consuming study of the effects produced in his patient by his illness, and an equally precise choice from his catalogue of hundreds of remedies, before he can be certain he has settled on the specific cure for a specific set of symptoms. While one case of whooping cough might be cured by a particular homeopathic remedy, the next, being slightly different, might require the administration of any one of perhaps twenty other substances.

Predictably, the practice of homeopathy attracted cranks as well as competent physicians—as late as 1922 a well-known manual of homeopathic remedies made the surprising assertion that the north pole of a magnet was good for toothache and the south pole would cure an ingrowing toenail.

Alexander Griffith was neither a crank nor a fanatic, as he demonstrated when his son Harold, at the age of three, contracted diphtheria—then and for many years afterwards a disease which often proved fatal. The "allopaths," as homeopaths called orthodox doctors, had just developed an antitoxin for diphtheria and Alexander, in the face of protests from his doubting colleagues, used it to pull the boy through. He continued, though, to have great faith in the plant extracts and other natural substances used in homeopathy. He used to joke that calendula solution, a homeopathic healing agent prepared from marigolds, helped him to become established in practice. During his first week in Montreal, where he settled after studying medicine in New York, a laborer came to visit him with a badly lacerated hand. Alexander stitched it up and bathed it with calendula solution. The wound healed so quickly that the man recommended the new doctor to all his friends.

Harold absorbed some of his father's interest in the action of natural substances on the human system and so years later when Wright drew his attention to curare he was perhaps more receptive to its possibilities than he might otherwise have been. He was influenced, also, by another homeopathic belief: that drugs, even natural ones, should be used in only minute quantities. "The proper dose of any drug," Harold Griffith said throughout his career, "is the smallest quantity that will get the job done." It was this conviction that led him into his continuing search for new anesthetic agents that would have fewer toxic effects on his patients. Curare was thus the culmination of a long personal quest, for its introduction ended forever the need to take patients to the brink of death with "knock-out" doses of anesthetics.

His father's homeopathy had still another influence on Harold Griffith's career: it led to the foundation of the hospital in which he spent his working life. Then, as now, homeopaths were considered little better than quacks by the medical establishment. Alexander and his colleagues, although qualified physicians, were not permitted to practice in Montreal's hospitals—a serious handicap to any doctor. So they decided to establish a hospital of their own. On the day Harold was born his father signed the deed to a three-story house near the center of town which became the Montreal Homeopathic Hospital. In addition to his practice, Alexander shouldered the responsibilities of medical director, a position he occupied—without pay—until his death. By this time the hospital—now called the Queen Elizabeth—had moved to a new building and had become a well-equipped general hospital with 275 beds, and he had seen one of his sons become its chief anesthesiologist and another its chief surgeon.

Harold's first personal experience of the hospital came in 1906, when he was twelve years old and his father diagnosed a pain in his right side as appendicitis. "What do you think?" the boy wrote in his diary. "I am going to have operation tomorrow. That means I won't take any more exams. Hurrah! HURRAH!" While his attitude toward his studies improved later, he was never a particularly brilliant pupil, though he usually managed to finish in the top quarter of his class.

The next diary entry was considerably less enthusiastic. "Had operation," it said. "The ether was *rotten!*" Griffith never forgot this early repugnance for what is probably still the world's most widely used anesthetic agent, though other substances have largely replaced it in the more medically advanced countries. Perhaps this boyhood experience prompted his lifelong readiness to experiment with any new anesthetic technique he thought might make operations not only safer but less unpleasant.

Griffith was twenty when his cosy world was shattered by the outbreak of World War I. He had always had weak eyes and since he was about to enter his second year of medicine at McGill University he could have remained safely at home. Instead, he enlisted immediately as a stretcher-bearer, overcoming his moral scruples long enough to bluff his way past the recruiting officer by memorizing the letters on the sight chart. His brief acquaintance with the theory of medicine behind him, he now faced a brutal introduction to its practice, in the muddy trenches of Europe. He became a sergeant and won the Military Medal in 1917 for gallantry under fire in the slaughter of Vimy Ridge, where more than eleven thousand of his fellow Canadians were killed or wounded.

The medal was ultimately delivered to his father back in Canada with a letter regretting that the brave soldier who had won it had not lived to receive it in person. The army had lost track of Griffith for a good reason. At this stage of the war, the Royal

Navy was running short of doctors and Britain was accepting boys with three years at medical school as "probationer surgeons." Griffith reasoned that he had gained more valuable experience in the trenches than he would have at college and prevailed upon his commanding officer to certify that he had the necessary three years' training. He finished the war in the comparative comfort of a berth as ship's "surgeon" aboard a British destroyer.

He returned to Canada in time to help his father in the great postwar influenza epidemic—"We had some interesting successes with homeopathic remedies," he said long afterwards—then resumed his studies at McGill with a store of practical experience some of his teachers might have envied, experience which he immediately began to put to good use. He paid for his tuition by giving anesthetics at weekends, mainly to children being circumcised or having their tonsils removed in doctors' offices, in conditions that appalled him when he recalled them in later years: "We would give them a whiff of ether, the doctor would force open their mouths and snip out the tonsils and then we would hold them over a bowl until they stopped bleeding."

Anesthesia had then been in use for more than half a century, but the technique by which it was administered had advanced little since Morton's day. Few doctors specialized in the art—it was still much more an art than a science—and anesthetics were usually given by any intern or student who happened to be around at the time. Inhalers with varying degrees of similarity to the one used by Morton had been developed, but more often than not the equipment was rudimentary: a bottle of ether or chloroform and a gauze pad held over the hapless patient's nose and mouth. The anesthetist dripped either ether or chloroform onto the pad in whatever quantity his experience suggested to him, and "going under" was an unpleasant ordeal.

Drugs which make the induction of anesthesia as easy as dozing off to sleep, such as Pentothal, were still years in the future. Students learning to administer ether were taught to recognize four stages of anesthesia. In the first, called the stage of analgesia, the patient's response to pain would be dulled but he would still be partly conscious. In the second stage, the anesthetic would have overcome the higher centers of the brain and the patient would be unconscious. But his subconscious would not yet have been subdued and he might involuntarily hold his breath, shout, or throw himself about. The third stage, called the stage of surgical anesthesia, enabled the surgeon to perform the operation, and the fourth stage—one that students dreaded to see—was the stage of impending overdose. Unless corrected, this led straight to the cessation first of breathing and then of the heart.

The struggles of a patient before his subconscious processes were subdued were often extremely violent, and several orderlies might be needed to hold a burly man down on the table. In later years, lecturing students, Griffith used to regale them with what he swore was a true account of an unnerving incident that once befell his father-in-law, who was also a doctor. On this occasion, as the patient sank into the second stage of anesthesia he suddenly leaped off the table and fled down the hospital corridor into the street, clad only in his nightshirt. The anesthetic was beginning to wear off as his doctors caught up with him and it was a puzzled patient they led back into the hospital: he had no recollection of making his dramatic bid to escape the knife. Griffith himself lost many a pair of glasses in these second-stage battles, before he could hand a motionless patient over to the surgeon.

Coming round from deep ether anesthesia in those days was even more of an ordeal than going under. Because of the apparently unavoidable curse of general intoxication, patients were at best acutely uncomfortable and at worst ill for hours or even days after their return to the surgical ward from the operating room.

While most doctors accepted this distressing situation as the inevitable tribute exacted for the boon of surgery, Griffith quickly saw that here, in anesthesia, there was a "real need" for improvement. It was, he decided, a field that offered both a challenge and the prospect for an ambitious young man of solid achievement. There was also a more mundane reason for him to specialize: his father's hospital still had no specialist in anesthesia on its staff.

By the time Griffith graduated he had given anesthetics to more than four hundred patients—indeed, on the day he wrote his final examination in surgery he administered the anesthetic to a fellow student undergoing an emergency operation for severe blood poisoning contracted while he was assisting at an autopsy on a man who had died from streptococcal meningitis. Griffith summed up his experiences in a paper that won second prize in the McGill Medical Society's senior competition. At this early stage in his career, he already displayed a concern for his patients that never left him: "It is very important that the anesthetist should secure the confidence of the patient. If they are not already acquainted it is well for him to meet the patient beforehand and say a reassuring word. The anesthetic room should be absolutely quiet, and it should be remembered that the patient's mental and physical comfort is the prime consideration, and not some irrelevant discussion by the doctors."

In 1925 Harold Griffith had an experience that was to govern the direction of his whole career; without the lesson it taught him, he might never have dared to use curare. A man of about forty came to his office one evening complaining of a hard lump in his scrotum. As Griffith completed his examination, the plainly nervous patient asked him, "What do you think, doctor?" Griffith struggled to retain the physician's mask of impassiveness. "I can't be sure yet," he said, trying to give his voice a note of confidence he did not feel. "I think we'd better have you in the hospital and check you over." But he already suspected what the diagnosis would be. There was a strong chance that the man had cancer, and Griffith contemplated the prospect with even more than the usual sadness felt by any doctor faced with this diagnosis. For only a few weeks earlier he had delivered the man's wife of a baby. "We'll give you a local anesthetic and do a thorough examination," he said. But the man protested immediately: "Oh no! If you're going to do an operation I want to be put right under so I won't know anything about it."

Here was a problem Griffith had not foreseen. The man sitting so nervously before him weighed four hundred pounds. The fat hung in rolls about his neck and his immense body wobbled grotesquely as he walked. It would be difficult to imagine a worse candidate for a general anesthetic. He wheezed with the effort of even normal breathing; his arteries would be narrowed by fat, placing his heart under a constant strain that would be greatly increased by the effect of a general anesthetic. Griffith tried to calm his fears and persuade him to accept the much lesser risk of a local anesthetic. But the man was adamant. It was imperative that the tumor be removed and examined for cancerous cells. Reluctantly, Griffith agreed to the general anesthetic. By now his father's hospital was equipped with a machine that enabled him to give a mixture of nitrous oxide, the safest anesthetic known, and oxygen. He would use this.

On the day selected for the operation, Griffith greeted his patient in the operating room clad in the traditional white gown and gauze mask—the green gowns used in modern operating rooms to lessen reflections and ease the strain on the eyes had not yet been adopted. The man was drowsy now and his nervousness had evaporated, thanks to the tranquilizing injection of morphine he had been given half an hour earlier. Griffith spoke reassuringly to him. "Just take a few deep breaths of this and you'll find yourself going off to sleep," he told him as he switched on his machine and placed the rubber mask over the patient's nose and mouth.

The man breathed in and out deliberately for a few moments and soon slipped away into unconsciousness. But almost immediately Griffith saw with alarm that he had stopped breathing. Quickly he reached for the regulating wheel on his gas machine, shut off the stream of nitrous oxide and switched to pure oxygen. It had no effect; something must be blocking the patient's trachea, or windpipe. Could his tongue have fallen back in his throat? Griffith whipped the mask off the man's face, grasped his tongue with a pair of forceps and drew it forward. But still he continued to suffocate.

This was the gravest possible emergency. Griffith replaced the mask and tried again by squeezing the rebreathing bag to force oxygen into the man's lungs. By now his brother, who was to perform the operation and had been "scrubbing up" on the other side of the room, had realized something was wrong and had come over to help. He started to press rhythmically on the patient's chest in an effort to force his motionless lungs into life. The man's face began to turn blue. While Griffith persevered with the flow of oxygen, his brother clambered up on the table and knelt astride the huge, recumbent figure to exert stronger pressure on his chest. Still the breathing did not begin.

There was only one course left; to cut into the neck and open a hole in the windpipe below whatever was blocking it so that oxygen could be pumped directly into the lungs. This is the operation—a tracheotomy—that was performed on Squire Waterton's donkey Wouralia. One reads occasionally in fiction of some bold doctor pulling out a penknife and performing it to save the life of an unfortunate accident victim who would otherwise have choked to death. It is not quite so easy as this would suggest. The windpipe, about the thickness of a man's finger, lies among a network of muscles, tendons, and blood vessels, and behind the thyroid gland. And in this patient James Griffith also had to contend with a four-inch layer of fat.

The man's face was dark blue as he made his first incision. The slicing of the knife into the flesh brought no answering spurt of blood, a sure sign that his circulation was failing. Before the knife could expose the windpipe, his heart had stopped beating. At that stage in history, there was nothing more the doctors could do. Their patient was dead.

Griffith's remorse was eased at the autopsy: not only was the tumor malignant, as he had feared, but the cancer had run wild through both kidneys and spread to the rest of the man's abdomen. There was nothing any doctor could have done, in 1925 or today, to save his life. There was, however—though hardly a handful of doctors then practiced it—something Griffith could have done to prevent him from dying on the operating table as soon as he inhaled the first few whiffs of gas. And he never again gave an anesthetic without being prepared to do it.

The man had died from a laryngeal spasm, an occasional complication of anesthesia in which a reflex action of the vocal cords locks them closed, blocking the upper end of the windpipe and preventing air from entering the lungs. Griffith knew that a few doctors had for years been experimenting with a form of anesthesia known as "endotracheal"—meaning "within the windpipe." This consisted of passing a flexible tube down the trachea and using it as the vehicle to convey either air or anesthetic into the lungs. The method was originally evolved soon after the introduction of anesthesia as a means of artificial respiration for use in emergencies. Later, it was found to be an effective method of introducing the anesthetic into the lungs when for some reason, perhaps because the surgeon was operating on the nose or mouth, it was not practicable to use the customary rubber mask.

Griffith realized that if he had had a tube in his unfortunate patient's mouth and down his trachea, his vocal cords would not have been able to lock shut and deprive him of oxygen; what doctors call his "airway" would have been kept open. From then on, maintaining a clear airway—a procedure regarded as fundamental in modern anesthesia—became almost an obsession with Griffith. He never again gave an anesthetic without having a tube beside him ready for instant use.

"Intubation," as the process of inserting a tube into the trachea is called, has another important advantage. Behind the trachea is the esophagus, or gullet, the pathway by which food travels from the mouth to the stomach. During the act of swallowing, the epiglottis, a piece of cartilage above the vocal cords, snaps shut to prevent food or anything else passing down the trachea into the lungs—"going down the wrong way." The epiglottis operates independently of our conscious control, as one of the body's many protective reflex actions. You can demonstrate this to yourself quite easily by trying to breathe at the same time as you swallow.

During normal sleep, the body's protective reflexes continue to operate. If your tongue falls back and blocks your windpipe you will snore, not suffocate. But the drugged sleep of anesthesia is not normal. It overcomes the reflexes—indeed it is part of the anesthesiologist's job to overcome them, so that the surgeon can work in a motionless field. However, as we have seen, the subconscious reflex activity of the body is the last to be overcome by anesthesia. It is also the first to return. Since vomiting is a protective reflex, it is quite possible for an unconscious patient to regurgitate the contents of his stomach, either in the early stages of anesthesia or as he begins to come around from it. If this happens, as it can quite easily, while the epiglottis is still paralyzed, particles of partly digested food may find their way from the back of the throat down the windpipe, with disastrous results. They may either block the windpipe, causing suffocation, or continue down into the lungs, causing possibly fatal damage.

This danger explains the apparently harsh practice of withholding food from patients for several hours before an operation. But the anesthesiologist cannot always be sure a patient has not eaten recently, and the presence of a tube in the trachea ensures that in case of an accident he will always be able to supply the lungs with oxygen. And if the tube is fitted with one of several types of inflatable cuff designed to make it a snug fit in the windpipe, there is no danger of any foreign substance—even blood from an operation in the throat—finding its way down into the lungs.

Endotracheal anesthesia is routine for many operations today, and in view of all its advantages it may seem strange that its value was ever doubted. But in 1925, when Harold Griffith lost his patient to laryngeal spasm, it was still a controversial technique. One reason for this is that before the advent of curare and other drugs to relax the muscles, intubation demanded considerable experience and skill. Few doctors had mastered the procedure and most believed the danger of damaging the throat or windpipe made it unjustified.

Though by no means the originator of the endotracheal technique, Griffith was one of its pioneers in North America. He decided it met a "real need" and his enthusiastic advocacy of the method undoubtedly helped to popularize it. At first he used a curved brass tube to keep the airway open but since this involved obvious danger to the tissues of the throat and trachea he soon switched to woven-silk catheters, which he inserted with the aid of a laryngoscope, an optical instrument normally used for examining the throat. As soon as the patient was anesthetized Griffith would remove the mask, lift up his chin, and insert the laryngoscope until he saw the epiglottis. Careful lifting of the epiglottis with the laryngoscope would reveal the vocal cords beneath it. The trick then was to slip the catheter between the cords quickly and without touching them, which would send them into spasm and block the trachea.

During this complicated maneuver, which is even more difficult than it sounds, the patient was breathing normal air so that there was a danger of the anesthetic wearing off. If Griffith was not able to get the tube in immediately he would have to replace the mask, give more anesthetic to relax the muscles again, and then try once more. All in all, it is perhaps not surprising that few doctors felt enough confidence in their dexterity to risk intubation. Nowadays, the muscular relaxation afforded by curare makes insertion of an endotracheal tube a much simpler matter.

Griffith soon found that the normal urethral catheters he was using were slimmer than he would have liked. He wrote to the supplier in France asking for thicker and thicker tubes, which were duly supplied and proved excellent for his purpose. And then one day he received a visit from the company's sales representative—who told him he had been instructed by the girls in the factory to find out more about this apparent breed of supermen being produced in Canada.

In 1928, three years after his patient had died on the operating table, Griffith went to Boston to read the first of more than seventy medical papers he was to deliver during his career. It described his technique of intubation and the operations in which it had been successfully used. Probably not more than ten percent of the anesthesiologists in his audience had ever inserted a tracheal tube and some of them remained convinced that the procedure was likely to do more harm than good. But it was Griffith's experience with intubation that gave him the confidence fourteen years later to defy others' fears and risk injecting curare into the veins of a living patient: he knew that whatever happened, even if the curare paralyzed his patient's lungs, he could keep him breathing indefinitely.

The operations described in Griffith's first paper were all performed with ethylene, his favorite agent at that time. A gas introduced to anesthesia in Chicago in 1923, ethylene has now been almost entirely superseded by newer substances. But it was the first serious rival to the three anesthetic agents in use since Morton's day: ether, nitrous oxide, and chloroform. Of these three old standbys, the last, chloroform, is now completely discredited, because of the number of deaths it has caused through the years, either by sudden heart failure on the operating table or destruction of the patient's liver within a few days of the operation.

Ether, despite its unpleasantness, is a safe, reliable, cheap, and easily portable anesthetic which is comparatively simple to administer. Being a liquid, it must be vaporized before administration, as gasoline is vaporized in an automobile engine. But this presents no problem—as witness the early practice of merely pouring it onto a gauze pad. It interferes with the patient's breathing and heart action less than some other substances. And it is fairly difficult to overdose a patient with it, so that it can be given in quantities sufficient to relax the muscles for surgery.

However, ether's drawbacks remain. Its sickly odor gives the patient a sense of suffocation if it is administered too rapidly. Its highly irritant vapor makes it unsuitable for patients with respiratory infections, and the increased secretion of saliva and mucus it causes can lead to postoperative pneumonia. During a long operation, the liver and kidneys and other organs of the body soak up ether vapor, producing various complex and undesirable metabolic disturbances. All these failings tend to delay a patient's recovery from ether anesthesia, if not actually to make him sick. Taken together, they add up to the general intoxication that caused Griffith and many other doctors to search for a better anesthetic. (The search for the *perfect* anesthetic is still going on, since all those discovered so far have disadvantages to balance their advantages.)

Nitrous oxide, Humphry Davy's "laughing gas," which could so easily have been the first substance to free the world from the pain of surgery, shares few of ether's drawbacks. Other things being equal—though in a science as complex as anesthesia they seldom are—gases have several advantages over vapors. They are more rapid in their action and, even more important, more rapidly eliminated from the body after the operation. It is a simple cycle: the gas is picked up from the lungs by the blood, circulated around the body back to the lungs, and then excreted from the lungs as the patient breathes out. The organs of the body do not soak up gases as they soak up ether vapor and the liver and kidneys are not subsequently burdened with their elimination.

In particular, nitrous oxide, had little effect on either the breathing or the heart, is more pleasant to inhale and quicker than ether in its action. It does not irritate the membranes and is almost free of unpleasant or harmful after-effects. It is the safest of all anesthetics. But before the advent of curare it had one major disadvantage: it was not powerful enough for those operations requiring complete muscular relaxation. Using nitrous oxide alone, the anesthetist could not put his patient far enough "under" unless he also starved him of oxygen. Ordinary air is composed of four parts nitrogen to one part oxygen. But if the anesthetist gave his patient that same proportion of oxygen—twenty percent—along with the nitrous oxide, he would be only lightly anesthetized.

The property that attracted Griffith to ethylene was its potency. It shared many of the good qualities of nitrous oxide, in that it had no poisonous side-effects and was innocuous in its action on the heart. But it could carry a higher proportion of oxygen than "laughing gas"—as much as twenty-five percent—and still give good relaxation. Similar in its chemical makeup to marsh gas, ethylene had been known for well over a century but it was introduced into anesthesia by a curious chance. In 1908, Chicago florists were dismayed to find that carnations kept in certain greenhouses invariably died. Plant physiologists called in to solve the problem discovered that the culprit was ethylene, which was present in small quantities in the gas used to illuminate the greenhouses. The leaky gas pipes were repaired and the good people of Chicago were once again assured of flowers for their buttonholes.

A gas that could kill flowers, however, aroused the curiosity of Arno Luckhardt, professor of physiology at the University of Chicago. What, he wondered, would it do to animals? Luckhardt was a busy man, and it was not until after World War I that he could get around to experimenting with ethylene. When he did, he found that it did not kill animals—but it anesthetized them. Luckhardt and his assistant, a medical student named Jay Bailey Carter, tried the gas on themselves and in 1923 published a paper on its anesthetic properties. Then they discovered that an anesthetist at the University of Toronto, W. Easson Brown, had published a paper describing the anesthetic effect of ethylene on animals just two weeks earlier.

By Sir William Osler's test, Luckhardt and Carter deserve credit for the introduction of ethylene, because it was in Chicago that its use on human patients was first popularized. But Canadian anesthesiologists, including Harold Griffith, quickly took up the new agent. Griffith wrote several papers on his experiences with it, yet ethylene did not have an easy passage. It was, its critics complained, too dangerous, because when combined in a certain proportion with air it was highly explosive.

This danger was genuine. There were several sharp but relatively harmless explosions with ethylene in the Presbyterian Hospital in Chicago soon after its introduction there, and later in other places there were some well-reported tragedies in which patients were killed. But as Griffith and other supporters of the new gas pointed out, ether itself and all the other general anesthetics then known, with the exception of nitrous oxide and chloroform, were inflammable or explosive in critical concentrations. No matter—there was a bitter controversy and many hospitals banned ethylene, including, oddly enough, one hospital where it was proved that the explosion had been caused by another anesthetic, not ethylene.

In all operating rooms, there is equipment which can generate a spark and ignite an explosive mixture if one is present—the surgeon's cautery, for instance, a sort of electric knife that cuts with an intense heat which has the valuable property of coagulating the blood in small vessels and preventing bleeding. One of the most tragic ethylene explosions occurred in an operating room in Baltimore where a surgeon was using a cautery inside a patient's mouth. The administration of the ethylene had been stopped for some time, but suddenly the unconscious patient vomited. His stomach apparently contained an explosive concentration of the gas, which ignited as soon as it came into contact with the hot cautery. The blast took place in the patient's mouth and killed him.

This was an obvious warning about the dangers of cauteries and other electric equipment when explosive anesthetics were used, and Griffith mentioned the incident in a paper discussing the explosion problem in 1931. He also drew attention to another danger: the sparks which could be generated by the presence of static electricity in the dry air of heated operating rooms during the winter. These sparks could easily be prevented by the installation of humidifiers, he said, and the danger could further be reduced by running the mixture of gas and oxygen over water in the gas machine. Griffith also recommended several other measures which are now commonplace, such as floors made of conducting material to lessen the possibility of static sparks. Even today, with all these precautions and more, fatal operating-room explosions still occur occasionally, but fortunately they are one of the lesser hazards of anesthesia and surgery.

Griffith used ethylene without any trouble for ten years, but his successes with it did not blind him to the fact that there was still a "real need" for better anesthesia, and when a new gas came along he investigated it enthusiastically. It was in 1929 that G. H. W. Lucas and V. E. Henderson at the University of Toronto, casting round for an anesthetic agent that would be even better than Easson Brown's ethylene, tried out a gas called propylene on animals. It did not work as well as they had expected it would from their analysis of its chemical structure. Perhaps,

185

they decided, it was not sufficiently pure. So they eliminated its impurities and tried it again. This time it did not work at all. What had happened? After some pondering, they decided that propylene's anesthetic properties must be contained in its impurities and sure enough, when they dosed their laboratory animals with the impurities they keeled over in a most satisfying fashion, always recovering none the worse for wear.

For some reason, cyclopropane, as the gas was called, was not tried on human patients at the University of Toronto. "They missed the boat," said Griffith years later—for cyclopropane proved to be an excellent anesthetic, though more tricky than some to administer. At first, the gas was found difficult to manufacture in pure form, so that it was four years before it was given its first human trials, by Ralph Waters, the great teacher at the University of Wisconsin. Soon after Waters blazed the trail, Griffith obtained some and in 1933 became the second anesthesiologist to use it on human patients.

He was delighted with its performance and it was his "workhorse" anesthetic for the next thirty years. Cyclopropane is powerful, it reaches the brain quickly and thus induces insensibility with very little excitement, and it has few undesirable after-effects. Also, and this was one of its properties that most appealed to Griffith, it retains its anesthetic effect even when given with large quantities of oxygen. In fact, whereas nitrous oxide must be administered in a mixture of at least eighty percent gas to twenty percent oxygen, cyclopropane gives good anesthesia in a mixture of fifteen percent gas to eighty-five percent oxygen. As Griffith pointed out in his first paper on the new agent: "My conception of anesthesia with the older gases is that we administer the gas, plus enough oxygen to keep the patient alive and in good condition. With cyclopropane, on the other hand, we administer oxygen with just enough of the anesthetic gas to keep the patient asleep."

However, like all other anesthetics, cyclopropane has its drawbacks: it tends to interfere with the breathing and cause the heart to beat irregularly, which can make it dangerous in unskilled hands. Griffith, experienced and careful and with his tubes always ready to support a patient's breathing, was undeterred by these handicaps. But some other anesthesiologists ran into

186

trouble with the new gas and for a time he was the center of a controversy that raged around it.

None of this dampened his enthusiasm and by 1939 he was able to report that he had used it in more than five thousand cases, without a single death on the operating table. By this time, also, the stocky little Canadian anesthesiologist with the barrel chest and austere rimless spectacles—an odd contrast with his genial nature and lively sense of humor—had become a familar figure at American medical meetings. He had no advanced academic honors and he represented no university or famous teaching hospital. But his obvious competence and wide-ranging knowledge of the technicalities of his calling had won him the respect and friendship of the leaders of his profession. And so, in 1940, when Wright began to seek someone to try out curare in the operating room, it was natural that among those he should approach would be Harold Griffith.

chapter

13

Wright and Griffith had first met in the early thirties and by 1940 they considered themselves old friends. But when Wright broached the subject of curare Griffith greeted his suggestion with an indulgent laugh, as so many others were to do. Sure, he agreed, it would be great if you could get muscular relaxation without poisoning your patient half to death with anesthetics. But curare! Into his mind flashed visions of frogs and cats stretched out lifeless in physiological laboratories. The thought of doing that to a human patient! Griffith shuddered and advised his friend to leave curare to those most likely to profit from it, the jungle hunters of the Amazon.

But in the months that followed his mind kept coming back to the idea. After all, it would certainly "meet a real need." And in spite of curare's cruel reputation, it was not a new drug. Its effects were well known. He recalled Claude Bernard's experiments with it and wondered whether perhaps its action might be more fleeting and less toxic in an intact human being than in a laboratory frog. Certainly, curare paralyzed the breathing. But he had been using endotracheal tubes for years now and was confident he could keep his patients alive long enough for the effects of the poison to wear off. Besides, if he ran into trouble, there was a drug that neutralized its action. Even though its jungle makers never knew an antidote to their "flying death," one was discovered in Europe in 1900: a drug called physostigmine, extracted from a West African ordeal poison made from the Calabar bean. Further chemical research resulted in a compound called prostigmine, which stimulates involuntary muscles and in addition to being used as an antidote to curare is prescribed in the treatment of a crippling muscular disorder, myasthenia gravis, whose symptoms are similar to those of curare poisoning.

No doubt Griffith would have had even fewer misgivings if his wide boyhood reading had included Squire Waterton's *Wanderings in South America*. Curare's paralysis of the lungs was what scared everyone who approached it. Yet more than a century earlier the Squire and Benjamin Collins Brodie had demonstrated that as long as a curarized animal was given artificial respiration its body would eventually neutralize the poison and it would recover. Griffith had never heard of this experiment. But independently he arrived at the same conclusion.

When he next saw Lew Wright, at a meeting of anesthesiologists in Montreal in 1941, he asked him, "Whatever happened to your idea about curare?" Wright replied in some disgust, "I can't get anybody to use the damned thing." He told Griffith that Rovenstine's young assistant Manny Papper had tried it out—and rejected it. And that Stuart Cullen had been so alarmed by its effect on his experimental dogs that he had not dared to risk it on human patients. But, Wright persisted, A. E. Bennett was using it in small doses in psychiatry and he didn't seem to be getting into trouble with it.

There and then Griffith made up his mind. "I decided I'd better not miss out on a good thing any longer," he told friends years afterwards. To Wright, he said: "Send me some and I'll try it."

As soon as Wright returned to New York he sent Griffith some vials of Intocostrin, together with all the reports he had assembled on its experimental use, in the Squibb research laboratories and elsewhere. As he studied these, Griffith became more than ever convinced that with the proper precautions curare could be a safe and valuable drug. He decided there was no point in doing more research on animals. Either it would work in human patients or it wouldn't. There was only one way to find out.

He chose as his human guinea pig a twenty-year-old plumber, active and perfectly fit until he had begun to be bothered by pains in his right side a few weeks earlier. Griffith had diagnosed the trouble as appendicitis and the man was about to undergo one of the most common of all surgical operations: the removal of his infected appendix before it could burst and spread its poison through his system. Since he was a healthy and muscular young man he would need a heavier-than-average dose of cyclopropane to give the surgeon adequate muscular relaxation. It would be a good test of the Intocostrin.

For several weeks Griffith had discussed his plans with his assistant, a lively dark-haired girl named Enid Johnson who had graduated from medical school five years earlier and was now completing her specialist training in anesthesia. But because he wanted an unbiased verdict on the extent of the muscular relaxation produced by curare he did not confide in the surgeon, Dr. George T. Novinger. At twenty-seven, Novinger was Griffith's junior by twenty years, the son of an American who had once been the hospital's chief surgeon.

At 9:15 A.M. on January 23, 1942, the young plumber was given an injection of morphine to lull him into drowsiness. At 10 A.M., unaware that he was to make medical history, he was wheeled into the operating room and Enid Johnson placed the rubber mask over his face and began to give him a mixture of cyclopropane and oxygen. As soon as he was unconscious, Griffith inserted an endotracheal tube, a routine precaution that was more vital than ever this morning.

As the nurse handed Novinger his scalpel, Griffith's experienced eyes made one last sweep around the familiar scene: at Enid Johnson, one hand on the rebreathing bag and the other on the patient's pulse, who nodded her signal that all was well; at the man's chest, rising and falling regularly; and lastly, at the hypodermic needle in his hand, containing five cubic centimeters of the deceptively innocent-looking amber fluid science had distilled from a batch of "flying death" bubbled down over a jungle campfire several years earlier by one of Richard Gill's witch-doctor friends.

Firmly, Novinger made his first incision, a three-inch-long cut through the skin and fat of the patient's lower abdomen, to the right of and below his navel. As the knife laid open the flesh Griffith reached for the man's arm, found a vein and slowly began to press the plunger of his hypodermic needle. His attitude now was all concentration, watching always for the slightest warning sign of trouble. As Novinger's darting hands quickly tied off the spurting blood vessels with catgut before going on to the next incision, Griffith cautiously continued to squeeze the plunger. It took him ninety seconds to inject three and a half cubic centimeters of the curare solution—only slightly more than a teaspoonful.

Then he paused to assess its effect, for five minutes that seemed much longer. Would it work? Was the patient still breathing properly? Was his heart beating normally? Anxiously he eyed the rebreathing bag and the young plumber's rhythmically moving chest, felt his pulse, questioned the intent Enid Johnson. Everything seemed to be under control, so to make sure he would have the full effect of the curare he injected the rest of the dose.

This was the critical moment. Griffith grasped the control wheel on the gas machine and gradually turned it to reduce the flow of cyclopropane. Peering into the now wide-open wound, he cut down on the anesthetic to the point at which, in every operation before this one, the patient's muscles would have recovered their tautness and the surgeon, his manipulations frustrated by their returning rigidity, would have asked for "more relaxation, please." Instead, Novinger worked on unconcernedly. Griffith's excitement mounted as his young colleague easily parted the strong crisscross network of abdominal muscles with his gloved fingers, found the peritoneum—the membrane covering the internal organs—held it up with a pair of artery forceps and cut into it with his surgical scissors.

A three-inch incision in the peritoneum disclosed the coiled intestines and Novinger put in his finger to feel for the appendix. He discovered that as a result of the man's recurring attacks of appendicitis—inflammation of the appendix caused by infection—this was going to be a more difficult operation than he had expected. The inflammation had caused adhesions which had bound the swollen and distorted appendix to the large bowel. Before he could clamp it off and remove it with his cautery, he had to extend his incisions in both the abdomen and the peritoneum.

191

This took him more time than usual, but to Griffith's elation the muscles remained soft and manageable and he did not have to ask for more relaxation.

Long before Novinger had completed the operation and stitched up the wound, Griffith was satisfied curare would work. With his endotracheal tube he had easily supported the patient's breathing and he had not needed to administer the antidote, prostigmine. The effect of the curare seemed to wear off naturally after about twenty minutes and in fact the operation was finished under normal cyclopropane.

An hour and a half after Novinger's first incision, the patient was on his way back to the ward. Would he recover normally? This was the only question still to be answered and Griffith had seldom paid more attention to a postoperative case. The man came round from the anesthetic shouting and excited, but this was not unusual in those days, and in fact it was a welcome sign that there were no lingering after-effects of the paralysis. By evening Griffith was satisfied that curare had a valuable place in anesthesia—so much so that he used it next day in an operation to remove a patient's gall bladder. He had momentary doubts a couple of days later when the young plumber's temperature suddenly rose to 103 degrees. But after treatment with one of the new sulfa drugs his temperature dropped and ten days later he walked out of the hospital, a trifle shakily but quite well again.

None of those who took part in that first operation, even Griffith himself, fully realized that it was destined to change the whole course of anesthesia, and through anesthesia, surgery. Novinger recalls that in those days "advances in anesthesia were becoming so rapid that none of us surgeons gave it a thought when one of our team-mates suggested the use of a new drug." But he does remember being "amazed at the fantastic muscle relaxation afforded me," and saying afterwards that "it was without doubt the easiest abdominal operation I had done in my short career."

Vastly more experienced than his colleagues, Harold Griffith was in the best position to appreciate curare's potential value, but as he said years later, "We really had no conception that it was going to be such a revolutionary procedure. We just said: 'It seems to have worked. We'd better try it on another one.'

I remember I was quite pleased, and discussing it with Enid Johnson I said, 'Perhaps we've struck on something.' But I don't remember any great sense of drama."

In this same conversation, he confessed to an omission that still bothered him. "It has always troubled my conscience," he said, "that we never told the man what we were going to do." But the regulations governing medical experiments in 1942 were much less stringent than they are today, as Griffith reflected in a speech in 1967: "Attitudes with regard to clinical research have changed so radically in recent years that it must be difficult for young doctors of the present generation to believe how free we were, even twenty-five years ago, to undertake any procedure which seemed to be a right thing to do. 'Let your conscience be your guide' was then a fairly safe principle to follow. Perhaps never again will there be an opportunity such as I had to try out a completely new kind of drug."

Within a few weeks of that first operation, Griffith gave curare to twenty-five patients varying in age from eighteen to seventy. Eloquent, if inelegant, testimony to the new technique's effectiveness came during an operation to cut out the hemorrhoids of a man weighing two hundred and fifty pounds. Finding his probing impeded by the rigidity of the man's anal muscles, the surgeon requested more relaxation. Griffith administered Intocostrin and a few moments later asked the surgeon if there was any improvement. "My God, yes," the surgeon replied. "I could drive a horse and cart in here now." (Such irreverent comments are more common in operating rooms than the austere comportment of surgeons in public might suggest; that they seldom, if ever, find their way into medical papers is a matter of regret to at least one of their readers.)

In July 1942 Griffith published an account of his findings in *Anesthesiology,* the journal of the American Society of Anesthesiologists, in an article signed by himself and Enid Johnson. Not for the first time in his career, he immediately found himself the central figure in a medical controversy. And it was not only in his own country that the prophet was without honor. Before he published his paper, he sent a copy of it to his friend Sir Robert Macintosh, professor of anesthesia at Oxford University and perhaps the foremost practitioner of the specialty in Britain. Recognizing that this was a revolutionary technique, entailing the use of a drug then regarded as lethal in the laboratory, Macintosh passed on the paper to the university's physiological department. The shocked report that came back dwelt exclusively on a formidable catalog of reasons why curare should on no account be used in anesthesia. In short, it stated that whoever had written the paper was utterly ignorant of everything that had ever been learned about the "flying death."

Curare's ugly heritage intimidated many doctors in North America, too, and Griffith was widely criticized for foolhardiness. He replied that the drug had been given plenty of pharmacological study before he used it; its effects were well understood and as his "guinea pigs" he cited the mental patients to whom A. E. Bennett had administered it. Had they not survived he would never have risked using it, and in fact, even though he had given bigger doses of Intocostrin than Bennett, he considered its use much safer in the operating room, by an anesthesiologist accustomed to supporting his patients' respiration, than in neuropsychiatry. The skeptics also complained that he had drawn conclusions from a ludicrously low number of cases—only twenty-five. To this, Griffith replied that he had not been conducting a comparative study of similar drugs; he had been in the unusual position of trying out a drug with an entirely new type of action which could not be compared with any other then in existence. It had worked, and he considered it quite safe for other anesthesiologists to try it and see for themselves if they found it equally useful.

Fortunately, some of them eventually did. First to follow Griffith's example in the United States was Stuart Cullen, in Iowa. Cullen had held high hopes for Intocostrin when Wright first gave him some to try out, and had been crestfallen when the strangled gasping of his experimental dogs convinced him curare was too dangerous ever to find a place in the anesthesiologist's armory. It is a tribute to his intellectual integrity that, after this disappointment, when he read Griffith's paper he did not join the chorus of denunciation that greeted it but instead resolved to give Intocostrin another trial.

Cullen injected curare into a human being for the first time in December 1942, and even though some of his early patients stopped breathing—one woman exhibited symptoms alarmingly similar to those of his experimental dogs—he found it easy to

194

complete the operations successfully under artificial respiration. Three months later he sent a manuscript copy of his first paper to Griffith with a letter that began: "To use the vernacular, we have 'gone off the deep end' with the use of curare, and have now used it in two hundred and fifty cases . . . Our surgeons, as well as ourselves, are enthusiastic about it." Cullen's first paper confirmed Griffith's results and repeated his warning about the necessity for the anesthesiologist to have some means of artificial respiration at hand when using curare. And now, with the example of the respected Cullen, as well as Griffith, before them, other U.S. anesthesiologists began to experiment with the new technique. All those who tried it, instead of merely reading about it with disbelief, quickly became enthusiastic about it.

Doctors in Europe, where so much of the early work on curare was done, were slower to introduce it to anesthesia—not because they failed to realize its value but because of the difficulty of obtaining the American Intocostrin during the war. And it was in Britain that the next great stride was made. In 1945 two brilliant anesthesiologists at the University of Liverpool, T. Cecil Gray and John Halton, began clinical trials with the alkaloid d-tubocurarine chloride, production of which had now been made possible by its isolation from Gill's *Chondodendron tomentosum* in the Squibb laboratories. Right away, Gray and Halton recognized curare's importance. On March 1, 1946, after using d-tubocurarine in more than a thousand operations, they presented a paper entitled "A Milestone in Anesthesia?" before the Royal Society of Medicine. In the light of all that has happened since, they could well have omitted the question mark.

Gray and Halton were even more alert than the American pioneers to the beneficent effects of the light anesthesia curare made possible, and they carried the new technique a bold stage further. Whereas in North America anesthesiologists tried to restrict the dose of curare to a level that would not paralyze the patient's breathing, Gray and Halton said that to take full advantage of the relaxation it afforded it should be administered in large doses—large enough to paralyze the respiratory muscles as a matter of course. This drastic step imposed upon the anesthesiologist the duty of breathing for the patient—"controlled respiration"—but it enabled operations to be conducted under extremely light anesthesia; so light that some critics called it "anesthesia without anesthesia."

Gray and Halton gave their patients just enough nitrous oxide to keep them asleep and insensible to pain, in a state of analgesia rather than true anesthesia. And, in the words of one of their former students, "they used curare by the bucketful," counteracting its effects at the end of the operation with prostigmine. It was a revolutionary technique but, said its authors, it was of tremendous benefit to all patients undergoing chest or abdominal operations.

Their paper made a vivid impression on the eminent doctors present when it was read to the Royal Society of Medicine, an impression that was heightened when Professor Charles A. Wells, head of the department of surgery at Liverpool University, rose to add the weight of his opinion to those of the anesthesiologists. "Every advance demands its own sacrifice," said Wells, "but in this instance there has been no human sacrifice." He was satisfied, he said, that thanks to the new technique many patients were alive and well that day who would not have survived other anesthetics, and successful operations had brought relief to still others who but for curare would have had to be written off as inoperable.

In the months that followed, doctors who tried out the Gray-Halton technique were amazed at how it transformed both the operation itself and the patient's recovery from it. Surgeons who had sometimes labored long and hard to replace recalcitrant organs and close an abdominal incision now found their job immeasurably easier. And patients subjected to major operations no longer lay for hours or days in a haze of suffering. Only minutes after the last stitch was inserted in their wounds they awoke feeling as fresh as they had before the anesthetic. Before long they were able to sit up in bed or take a few hesitant steps—activity which hastened their recovery and helped to prevent the lung complications which had so often afflicted patients who after an operation were unable or unwilling, because of the pain it caused, to cough and breathe deeply and thus clear their lungs of mucus and the threat of infection. As the use of the new technique quickly spread, not only in Britain but elsewhere, its value became obvious.

A century earlier, anesthesia had parted the ancient insepara-

196

bles: surgery and pain. Now a new drug had come to anesthesia, making it at once safer and much less unpleasant. More "poor-risk" patients, the chronically ill, the weak, and the old were now able to benefit from the surgeon's knife; fewer patients died in the days following an operation and there was less and less occasion for that only half-humorous verdict: "The operation was a success but the patient died."

It was a spectacular achievement—and as much a beginning as an end. Curare went on to make a fundamental change in the whole philosophy and practice of anesthesia. In a series of later papers, Cecil Gray developed a concept that became known as "triad anesthesia," in which the anesthesiologist achieved the three essentials of anesthesia—sleep, freedom from pain, and muscular relaxation—with small doses of the separate drugs each capable of producing one of these desirable effects. Hitherto, general anesthesia had been something like hunting with a shot-gun: the anesthesiologist fired one cartridge—his toxic dose of the anesthetic—trusting that some among the hail of pellets would score hits on the various bodily systems he needed to overcome. Inevitably, stray pellets would hit something he did not want to injure. Now, for the first time, curare enabled him to separate his targets, to attack each accurately with a specific drug designed to bring about a specific effect and cause as little interference as possible with other bodily activities. And now that he could attack each target separately, he could also study it separately. One after another, in exciting progression, new discoveries were made about the physiology of breathing, the transmission of nerve impulses, and the many other phenomena involved in anesthesia. Curare not only banished "general intoxication" from the operating room; it made a precise science out of what had for a century been an imperfect art. And the discoveries to which it led gave the anesthesiologist his present power to shepherd patients safely through operations of a complexity and severity undreamed of only a few years ago.

Soon after Gray's first paper, as more and more doctors sought supplies of d-tubocurarine, European drug manufacturers began to cast around for a synthetic substitute for the natural drug. Wartime shortages were still fresh in their minds and since Latin America seemed likely to be among the more politically unstable areas of the world, there was a chance that some future war or revolution might cut off shipments of the raw poison from the jungle. Also, it was thought that a thorough laboratory search for substances with a similar chemical makeup to the original might unearth a relaxant drug which did not dangerously depress the breathing. This has so far proved an unattainable ideal, though curiously the nearest approach to it was the first artificial "curare," which raised high hopes when it was introduced to Britain in 1947.

Mephenesin (sold under the trade names Myanesin in Britain and Tolserol in the United States) acted on the spinal cord rather than the myoneural junction. But it gave a reasonable degree of relaxation without interfering too much with the breathing. Unhappily, it also had tragic side-effects when injected into the bloodstream. In some patients it caused hemolysis, an intractable condition in which the red blood cells burst and their hemoglobin, having escaped into the blood plasma, is carried to the kidneys, where it blocks their action and causes them to fail. After a number of patients died—their lives could have been saved today by artificial kidneys—it was only too apparent that mephenesin had no future as a relaxant. It was then prescribed in tablet form as "a sedative in psychological conditions associated with anxiety and tension." This time the side-effects were more bizarre than tragic—it turned some brunettes into blondes. (Whether this aggravated or eased their anxiety was not recorded.) Ill-starred though it was, mephenesin did have a soothing effect on some disturbed patients and the interest it prompted led to further research which resulted in a closely related chemical becoming the first true tranquilizer, the famous—or notorious, according to your point of view—Miltown.

In the next few years, a bewildering variety of drugs bearing little apparent relationship to either curare or each other arose to contend for the title of the "ideal" muscle relaxant. Medical literature was littered with the tongue-twisting names of such substances as "the di-iodoethylate of bis (quinoleloxy) pentane," "heterocyclic decamethylene bis-quaternary ammonium salts," and "benzoquinonium chloride," mercifully also known as Win 2747. If these sample appellations intimidate the reader, many anesthesiologists were hardly less confused. Each new agent had, or was supposed to have, its own desirable properties but more were found wanting than found their way into practical use, and

198

none has ever supplanted the alkaloid *d*-tubocurarine, extracted from the tarry mess compounded in the Amazonian jungles. In fact, some anesthesiologists who had been using other relaxants have in recent years returned to *d*-tubocurarine, if only because in prostigmine it has a sure antidote—a reassuring asset shared by only one of its synthetic competitors, gallamine.

The lack of an antidote is no problem with one of the most commonly used curare substitutes, succinylcholine. Whereas a single injection of the natural drug may relax a patient's muscles for as much as twenty minutes, the effect of succinylcholine wears off almost immediately. The anesthesiologist administers it by the technique known as "intravenous drip"—feeding it into a vein through a plastic tube throughout the operation. Its fleeting action enables him to switch relaxation on or off according to the needs of the surgeon.

Personal preference and familiarity with a particular drug often govern the anesthesiologist's choice of relaxant. Gallamine, sold under the trade name Flaxedil, was introduced in France in 1947 and it owes its present popularity to the fact that it combines well with halothane, one of the newest and most successful anesthetics. Widely used on both sides of the Atlantic, halothane is a liquid, like chloroform, which it somewhat resembles. It was developed in Britain and introduced to practice there in 1957. By no means perfect—it can interfere with the action of the heart and bring on a lowering of the blood pressure—halothane nevertheless has many advantages: it is potent, comparatively safe, and causes little discomfort to the patient. Above all, it will not explode or burn.

Halothane was introduced to the United States in 1958 and was greeted so enthusiastically that by 1963, five years later, it had been administered to about ten million Americans. But then came disturbing news. Several hospitals reported that some patients who had been given it later developed severe liver trouble —even complete liver destruction, which is, of course, fatal. At least ten deaths were reported. Ten deaths in ten million cases might seem a modest number, but when a patient lies on an operating table he delivers his life into the anesthesiologist's hands, and anesthesiologists do not take their stewardship lightly. Halothane's similarity to chloroform was known—and so was chloroform's potentially damaging effect on the liver. Even before news of the deaths became public property, which it did in the spring of 1963, a thorough investigation had been launched by the committee on anesthesia of the National Academy of Sciences-National Research Council. Over a period of four years, the committee studied 856,515 operations carried out with various general anesthetics. It reported in 1966 that fatal damage to the liver was a rare occurrence which could usually be attributed to shock or previous liver disease. While the possibility of its causing an occasional death could not be entirely ruled out, halothane, rather than being a dangerous anesthetic, actually had a better-than-average safety record. Within six weeks of their operations, 1.87 percent of those patients who had received halothane were dead, compared with an average figure for all anesthetics of 1.93 per cent.

These figures do not, of course, mean that two out of every hundred people undergoing an operation die from the effects of the anesthetic; they include postoperative deaths from all causes, among which may be the surgical procedure or the illness that made the operation necessary in the first place. It is often difficult, even after an autopsy, to say definitely that a death was caused by an anesthetic, and estimates of anesthesia death rates vary from one death in two thousand or so cases to one death in fifteen thousand cases. The difficulties are even greater when it comes to determining the relative safety of different anesthetic agents. Ideally, an anesthesiologist trying to assess the respective merits of two anesthetics would administer each one to a similar number of patients undergoing similar operations and compare their effects. But general anesthetics have many different effects on the bodily mechanism and not all patients react to them in the same way. No matter how carefully the anesthesiologist monitors a patient's heart during an operation, for instance, he cannot be sure that it is being affected only by the anesthetic. Its action may vary according to what the surgeon is doing, how fast the patient is losing blood, and what other drugs have been taken. With so many variable factors, accurate statistics about the relative merits of various anesthetics, and their safety, are always difficult to come by. And even when statistics are gathered, there is not always agreement about the way they are interpreted.

A classic example of these difficulties—and the lively dissension they can provoke—occurred in 1954, twelve years after

Harold Griffith's young plumber had his fateful operation in Montreal. Two Harvard anesthesiologists, Dr. Henry K. Beecher, chief of anesthesia at Massachusetts General Hospital, and his associate, Dr. Donald P. Todd, startled the medical world, which by now had long since accepted the value of relaxants, with a long and detailed paper entitled "A Study of the Deaths Associated with Anesthesia and Surgery." Beecher and Todd had arranged that in each of ten U.S. university hospitals a surgeon and an anesthesiologist would analyze every case handled and every death occurring on the surgical wards during a five-year period from 1948 to 1952 and assign deaths to one of the following categories: the patient's disease, an error in diagnosis, an error in surgical judgment, an error in surgical technique, or an "anesthesia death." The survey took in a total of 599,548 administrations of anesthesia.

After studying the figures they had collected and setting them out in thirty-three tables, Beecher and Todd concluded that a surgical patient admitted to any of the ten hospitals had one chance in seventy-five of dying. There was one chance in ninety-five that he would succumb to the disease which brought him to the hospital, and one chance in 420 that his death would be caused by an error in diagnosis or surgical judgment or technique. There was one chance in 1560 that anesthesia would be an important contributing cause of his death, and one chance in 2680 that anesthesia would be its "primary" cause.

But the most alarming finding—a finding that immediately had anesthesiologists on both sides of the Atlantic up in arms—was that whenever curare or one of the other relaxants was used the anesthesia death rate increased almost six times. This was a staggering allegation, and if true it was a damaging blow to a technique that anesthesiologists, and surgeons, were finding increasingly valuable.

The reaction was fast—and furious. At least one senior anesthesiologist in a hospital which had taken part in the study wrote to Beecher saying that whatever his overall figures showed, they did not reflect *his* hospital's experience with curare. No fewer than sixteen M.D.s signed a letter to the journal that had published the Beecher report, the *Annals of Surgery,* alleging that its conclusions were not justified by the statistics presented. To support their charge, they pointed out that Beecher had

201

concluded from the statistics that the use of ether had increased by 45 percent during the five-year survey; interpreted another way, they claimed, the same figures proved that there had been a 6.7 percent *decrease* in the use of ether. Other anesthesiologists, unwilling or unable to dispute either Beecher's facts or his findings, claimed they merely underscored the importance of the warnings sounded from the start by Griffith, Cullen, and Gray and the other pioneers: that curare was a dangerous poison demanding the utmost respect, but that it was safe when used by skilled anesthesiologists ready and able to support the patient's breathing. English anesthesiologists, in particular, felt that many of their American colleagues lacked a proper understanding of what constituted "adequate" artificial respiration and had been too slow to adopt Gray's technique of *controlling* the respiration and then reversing the curare's effect at the end with a heavy dose of prostigmine. (Whereas English anesthesiologists quite often gave prostigmine in five-milligram doses, it was put up by American drug companies in half-milligram ampuls; this meant a U.S. anesthesiologist would have to open ten ampuls to give what an English doctor would consider an adequate antidote. Perhaps because of this, American anesthesiologists have always been more dubious about the effectiveness of prostigmine than their British counterparts.)

The controversy over whether Beecher's statistics accurately reflected the situation in the United States at that time, whether in fact curare really did increase the risks of anesthesia sixfold, has never been entirely resolved. Beecher himself is satisfied now that whatever the position at the time of his survey, his figures certainly would not hold today. "We have learned a great deal about the utilization of curare and curare-type drugs," he says. The Beecher-Todd survey was probably useful in once again reinforcing the warnings that muscle relaxants were potentially lethal and must only be used with great care. But it did little to halt their spreading use, except perhaps indirectly, and temporarily, in the U.S. armed forces.

The survey was made possible by a grant from the U. S. Army's medical research and development board, which Beecher praised as a fine example of how military support could benefit civilian medicine. But some anesthesiologists still feel that this particular case of military-civilian cooperation had less happy results for the armed services: they believe that what became known as "the Beecher school" of opposition to curare influenced the army to withhold the use of relaxants during the Korean War. Beecher himself indignantly rejects this idea as "absurd," pointing out that while he himself was in Korea with the First Marine Division in 1950, his report was not published until 1954. On the other hand, he had begun to collect his statistics in 1948, and the evidence implicating curare in anesthesia deaths was so startling that it might have been expected to show up early in the survey. Given its official connection with a study that was to prove so critical of curare, it would have been understandable if the Army had approached the whole question of muscle relaxants with some reserve.

Whatever the reason, there is no doubt that the use of curare was not sanctioned in Korea. In the fall of 1952, Major Charles F. Egan, a Canadian anesthesiologist who had just returned from a year in command of Canada's special forward surgical unit there, told a congress of anesthesiologists at Virginia Beach that not only were relaxants unavailable at the front but "visiting surgical consultants from Army headquarters in Japan stated dogmatically that curare was a dangerous drug and should never be used." Fortunately, Egan added, he had taken his own supply of curare with him, "for there is not the least shadow of a doubt that it alone meant the difference of life over death in some last-ditch cases."

Egan, who later taught at McGill University in Montreal and then went into practice in Wyandotte, Michigan, was referring to the large number of casualties with severe shock, which commonly accompanies battle wounds. The term "shock," which describes a dangerous condition that doctors do not yet fully understand, confuses laymen, suggesting as it does that it is somehow brought on by a bad fright. Certainly, shock can be caused by emotional stress after an injury, but it can also develop in an unconscious person who is quite unaware of any fear: not so many years ago it was the most common cause of death after surgery. Shock can be caused by loss of blood, by an overwhelming infection, or by drugs. Essentially, it is a sudden depression of vital nerve centers that produces a rapid and serious fall in the blood pressure. For some unknown reason, the plasma, the clear fluid of the blood, leaks away through the walls of the capillaries

203

in the extremities—the shock victim's skin is pale and his hands and feet are usually deathly cold. Deprived of its plasma, the rest of the blood becomes thick and sluggish and the heart beats faster than usual with the effort of trying to circulate it around the body. There are various kinds of shock—wound shock differs from burn shock, for instance, and both differ from the type of shock suffered by a heart-attack victim. But doctors believe it is involved in some way in most deaths.

Virtually all that is known about shock has been learned only in recent times. The ghastly bloodletting of World War I focused attention on the problem but in those days doctors could do little for shock victims other than keep them warm and watch help-lessly as they died, which they did in their thousands. By World War II, transfusions of plasma or whole blood had improved the picture and many lives were saved by them. But surgeons were still unable to operate on a person in a severe state of shock, since the anesthetic was only too likely to cause a further, and fatal, depres-sion of the patient's system. Even today, doctors prefer to bring patients out of shock before beginning an operation, by giving them blood or plasma transfusions—and, of all things, injections of sodium bicarbonate to counteract the dangerous acidity which builds up in tissues starved of blood. This is not always possible, though, and in those emergencies where an operation on a shock patient must be done right away curare is a life-saver—by ena-bling it to be performed with much lighter anesthesia and there-fore far less stress on the already-weakened patient's system.

Battle casualties had a better chance of survival in Korea than in any previous war: only two percent of those wounded died, compared with four percent in World War II. This was achieved partly by the extensive use of helicopters to ferry casualties quickly back to medical aid, and partly by the better care of the wounded which medical advances and the experience gained in World War II made possible. A fifty-percent reduction in the death rate is an outstanding achievement in any field of medical en-deavor. But one wonders whether the improvement might not have been even more spectacular had it not been for the Cin-derella status that anesthesia seems to have had so much difficulty in shaking off. In his address to the anesthesiologists at Virginia Beach, Egan mentioned one U.S. surgical unit where the nurse-anesthetists were not able to perform endotracheal intubation.

"The death rate there," he said, "was three or four times as high as in the other surgical units." Had more skilled and experienced anesthesiologists been available in Korea, perhaps relaxants would have been available too; in which case, servicemen wounded in action and suffering from shock would have had the same access as their fellow citizens to the life-saving advances in anesthesia curare was making possible back home. (Relaxants were in common use in the U.S. armed forces by the time the Vietnam War came along.)

In the same month that Egan was describing his experiences in Korea, doctors in another small country on the opposite side of the world were fighting a different kind of war—a war in which each tactical success was a human life saved. In the summer and fall of 1952, Danish doctors were faced with the worst epidemic of poliomyelitis in European memory. Less than three years later, Dr. Jonas Salk was to announce the first of the vaccines that spelt the beginning of the end of polio as a major health scourge. But in 1952 doctors could still do nothing for the worst cases of the disease other than stand by impotently watching them die.

Poliomyelitis is an inflammation of the central nervous system caused by a virus. Many of those who contract it do not develop the dreaded paralysis, probably because of some natural resistance to the disease. But it attacks the spinal cord and the higher up the cord it rises the more muscles essential for respiration are paralyzed. The nerve center that controls breathing is in the medulla oblongata, the lowest part of the brain, where the top of the spinal cord begins to broaden. If this vital center is affected, the patient's breathing will be paralyzed and even with some form of artificial respiration he will often die.

The Danish epidemic overwhelmed doctors at Blegdam Hospital, Copenhagen's only hospital for the treatment of communicable diseases, where more than three thousand polio cases were admitted in seven months, 1250 of them with some degree of paralysis. At times there were as many as seventy patients requiring artificial respiration simultaneously—in a hospital which started the epidemic with one "iron lung" and six mechanical respirators. Facing what he described as "a major castastrophe," Dr. H. C. A. Lassen, Blegdam's chief physician, was near desperation. But he knew something of the recent advances in anesthesia, and he rea-

205

soned that if anesthesiologists could keep their patients alive when their lungs were artificially paralyzed by curare perhaps they could do something for patients whose breathing was paralyzed by polio.

Lassen appealed for help to Dr. Bjørn Ibsen, chief anesthesiologist in one of Copenhagen's big municipal hospitals, who immediately mounted an ingenious rescue campaign. First, Ibsen rigged up an easily duplicated emergency respirator that was essentially a stripped-down anesthetic machine: it consisted of a tank of oxygen with rubber tubes and reducing valves leading to a rebreathing bag and an endotracheal tube. When a patient developed respiratory paralysis a tracheotomy was performed and the tube inserted in his windpipe; his lungs could then be inflated with oxygen indefinitely as long as someone sat by his bedside squeezing the bag. Ibsen organized a thousand medical students to take on this task, working in relays, and some of the patients were kept alive by this simple method for more than three months. Before Ibsen was called in, 87 percent of patients with respiratory paralysis died; afterwards, only 37 percent of them died.

Ibsen's adaptation of an anesthetic technique to a completely different situation saved a hundred and twenty lives during the next six months; it also taught doctors around the world more than they had ever known before about the management of artificial respiration, and in so doing prepared the ground for major discoveries about the crucial importance of adequate breathing to every organ—and indeed to each of the billions of cells— in the human body. Gray and Halton in England had already pointed out that it was illogical to give a patient a drug that paralyzed his breathing muscles and then expect him to breathe for himself; this function must be taken over for him, as the price of securing complete relaxation. It is difficult in the light of present knowledge to appreciate what a revolutionary approach this was. The patient's breathing was possibly the most important life sign, closely watched by every anesthesiologist throughout the operation. If a patient stopped breathing on the operating table, the whole surgical team sprang to emergency stations; the surgeon ceased work immediately and everything else was subordinated to the work of resuscitation. For an anesthesiologist to stop the breathing deliberately seemed a wanton interference with nature; if nothing else, it deprived him of a sure way of telling that the patient was alive. But Gray and Halton proved it could be done.

Now, building on the careful Danes' experience, medical researchers were to find that far from being a foolhardy tampering with natural processes, to be undertaken only with extreme reluctance, controlling the patient's respiration had tremendous, though hitherto unsuspected, positive benefits.

As month followed month and the Copenhagen medical students toiled away at the monotonous task of squeezing their rebreathing bags a fixed number of times per minute, the doctors gradually realized that many of the symptoms which had been attributed to the paralytic form of polio actually stemmed from the patient's inability to breathe adequately. The dangers of not getting enough oxygen are readily understood by everyone; what now came to be recognized was that it is perfectly possible for a patient to be getting enough oxygen and yet for his body to be gradually poisoned by carbon dioxide, a damaging process which, if allowed to continue, can lead to convulsions and, ultimately, death.

The oxygen and other vital "foods" such as sugar and hormones which are carried around the body by the blood are burned down by normal healthy cells into carbon dioxide, which the blood carries away in exchange for the oxygen. A similar exchange takes place in the lungs: we breathe in air and breathe out the waste carbon dioxide. This, of course, is known to every schoolboy, and years ago when closed-circuit anesthesia was introduced—a system in which the patient breathes the same mixture of air or oxygen and anesthetic over and over again—the air he breathed out was purified by being passed through a canister of soda lime, a chemical with a great capacity for absorbing carbon dioxide.

As it absorbs carbon dioxide, soda lime changes color—from pink to blue, for instance. The old-time anesthetist watched for this change and it was a comforting assurance to him that the carbon dioxide was being extracted from his patient's breath. Unfortunately, this was not the whole story. As a result of the Danish polio epidemic, and the growing use of curare in the operating room, it was gradually realized that the efficiency of the oxygen-for-carbon dioxide exchange is impaired if the breathing is too shallow. So that when patients were left to breathe for themselves during a long operation, with at most an occasional squeeze of the rebreathing bag to "assist" respiration, the ex-

207

change process broke down. The anesthetist made sure his patient received enough oxygen, and from the evidence of his canister of soda lime he knew the carbon dioxide was being removed from the expired breath. The trouble was that not enough carbon dioxide was getting into the expired breath in the first place; too much of it was remaining in the patient's system.

Though relatively harmless for a short time, this building up of carbon dioxide in the body became increasingly more damaging in longer operations, because of its effect on the blood. Blood, as the old saying goes, is thicker than water. But it is like water in one important respect: the acids and alkalis it contains virtually cancel each other out. Normal blood is delicately balanced between acidity and alkalinity and it is vital to the healthy working of the body that this neutral balance be maintained. When too much carbon dioxide accumulates in the blood it disturbs this "acid-base balance" and causes, in the immortal advertising phrase, "excess acidity." This phenomenon, recognized only in the past fifteen years or so, has multifarious repercussions on just about every organ in the body, all of them undesirable and, if permitted to continue, disastrous. If the blood becomes too acid, for instance, it depresses the action of the heart and the circulation; as a further complication, it stimulates the body's secretion of adrenalin, which contracts the small blood vessels and slows the circulation even more. This can lead to a dangerous condition known as "metabolic acidosis," in which the body's cells find themselves unable to reduce the acids they absorb from the blood into carbon dioxide for elimination. If uncorrected, the accumulation of acids in the cells eventually proves fatal.

Realization of the problem of acidosis dispelled the last shreds of doubt about the wisdom of controlled respiration: it was clearly essential that carbon dioxide be fully eliminated from the anesthetized patient's system. And if he could not do this for himself when left to breathe naturally, then the anesthesiologist must do it for him. Intubation, and artifical "ventilation" of the lungs, as it is called, became routine for all but the simplest and briefest operations performed under general anesthesia. New, improved mechanical respirators were developed to shoulder this responsibility and the anesthesiologist in a modern operation sets them to deliver exactly the required amount of ventilation per minute, which he calculates from tables on the basis of the patient's height, weight, and physical condition. This normally prevents the development of acidosis, but to be on the safe side the anesthesiologist constantly monitors the acid-base balance of the patient's blood; he measures its levels of certain critical chemicals such as sodium and potassium; he checks the output of the heart and its effect on the circulation; and he maintains the normal blood volume by replacing fluids lost during the operation.

Science, in short, has supplanted guesswork—even the inspired, educated guesswork that made anesthesia an art. This is the real revolution curare has brought to the operating room, the true measure of its contribution to the welfare of mankind. It is this complex new science that enables the modern anesthesiologist to conduct his patients safely and in relative comfort through operations so drastic they simply could not have been imagined on that day not so long ago when Richard Gill stepped ashore in New York with the twenty-five pounds of curare he had gathered in the jungles of Ecuador.

And out of the anesthesiologist's mastery of that science have grown important new responsibilities and a new power to save life outside the operating room. His ability to control the patient's breathing for long periods, and to keep him in good condition while so doing, has led to the creation of "respiratory units" in the larger general hospitals of most cities. These have proved invaluable in the treatment of sufferers from chronic lung diseases such as silicosis or emphysema, patients whose chests have been crushed in car crashes or industrial accidents, and those whose breathing has been almost stopped by an overdose of drugs— whether by accident or design.

A pair of human lungs weighs about two and a half pounds. Essentially, they consist of millions of fine tubes, all branches and sub-branches of the windpipe. If the walls of all these tubes could somehow be unfolded and laid flat on the ground their total surface area would be about the size of a tennis court. Each tube has a rounded, bulbous end called an alveolus, and estimates of the number of alveoli in an average pair of lungs range from 300 million to 750 million. The alveoli are laced with tiny blood capillaries, whose walls are only a few hundred-thousandths of an inch thick. In a normal day, a normal man breathes in about 3300 gallons, or 530 cubic feet, of air. As each inhalation of breath fills this intricate network of tubes, the alveoli expand rather like a child's balloon being blown up, and the red blood cells passing through their capillaries absorb oxygen from the air and give up their carbon dioxide in exchange. The blood and the air do not actually come into contact: the exchange takes place through the fine walls of the alveoli.

This oxygen-for-carbon dioxide exchange, as we have seen, is essential to the human body. But there are some diseases which interfere with it. In silicosis, for instance, the dust breathed in over long periods by miners or men who clean stone buildings with sand-blasting machinery irritates the delicate membranes of the lungs and eventually produces a build-up of scar tissue which prevents the oxygen and carbon dioxide molecules from passing through the walls of the alveoli. A similar disease, whose dangers were slower to be appreciated, is asbestosis, caused by the inhalation of asbestos dust.

The exchange process is impaired in a different way in another disease, emphysema, whose cause is not yet understood, though chronic bronchitis may predispose a person toward it and many doctors believe it is in some way connected with air pollution. In emphysema, the alveoli lose their elasticity, like a balloon that has been inflated too often, and fail to contract when the patient breathes out. Breathing thus becomes difficult, and ultimately impossible.

Though these diseases are eventually fatal, their progression can sometimes be slowed down and their victims, while some of them may not be healthy enough to work, may live on for a number of years. There are plenty of men leading a normal life today on only one lung, and men have known to survive on only a fifth of their normal lung capacity. But patients with advanced silicosis or emphysema are known as "respiratory cripples," and for them an infection as simple as the common cold can often mean death: their lungs just do not have the reserve capacity to carry them through the illness.

In today's hospitals, respiratory units, using techniques borrowed from anesthesia, save many of these patients' lives during these emergencies: mechanical respiration, the forcing of air into their lungs, keeps them alive through the acute phase of the infection and enables it to be treated with drugs.

While the plight of an injured motorist with a crushed chest differs from that of a silicosis sufferer, the same technique of controlled respiration is used in respiratory units to save his life. Under normal conditions, the chest is a closed compartment; the only way for air to enter it is into the lungs through the windpipe. The negative pressure within this compartment holds the inflated lungs against the chest wall—if the compartment is broached and air gets in, the lungs collapse and shrink to the size of a closed fist. To accomplish the act of inhaling, the diaphragm, the muscle that forms the floor of the compartment, exerts a strong downward pull, and the rib muscles pull outwards. The effect of this pull is to enlarge the chest cavity, and the lungs, clinging to the chest wall, expand with it. Nature, as every schoolboy is taught, abhors a vacuum, so as the size of the lungs is enlarged air rushes in to fill up the extra space. For the lungs to be expanded in this way, of course, the whole chest structure must be rigid.

Unfortunately, even since the introduction of seat belts and collapsible steering wheels, a common occurrence in car accidents is for the driver to be hurled forward against the steering wheel or the dashboard with such force that most or even all of his ribs are broken. The chest compartment is then no longer rigid and when the diaphragm exerts its downward pull the ribs, instead of expanding the chest cavity, respond to the rule about vacuums and cave inwards. The lungs are thus unable to expand and the patient may suffocate. In the days before controlled respiration was understood, he usually did. Nowadays, in the respiratory unit, his lungs are mechanically inflated, if necessary for weeks, until his ribs have a chance to heal and restore the rigidity of the chest compartment.

In many hospitals, an anesthesiologist is in charge of the respiratory unit; in others, he is on call as a consultant. Sometimes, he will intubate his patient with an endotracheal tube. In a case of barbiturate poisoning, for instance, where the patient is unconscious, the tube can be tolerated for a couple of days, which is usually long enough for the drug to be eliminated from his system, either by his own kidneys or an artificial one, enabling him to resume breathing on his own. If you are fully conscious, however, you cannot tolerate an endotracheal tube stuffed down your throat, so in those cases where a conscious patient's breathing has to be maintained for some length of time, a tracheotomy is performed and the tube is inserted directly into the windpipe.

211

The creation of respiratory units has been the most important by-product of the anesthesiologist's new-found ability to keep his patient alive and in good condition throughout long periods of artificial respiration by constant monitoring of his bodily systems and careful maintenance of both the normal acid-base balance of the blood and its correct concentrations of oxygen and various other vital elements. But the new knowledge taught by curare has had another important result: it has at long last fulfilled the century-old dream that "the American poison" might be effective in the treatment of tetanus. Accepted treatment for this disease now is to abolish its fatal convulsions with curare for as long as it takes the doctors to fight and conquer the disease itself with antitetanus serums.

The case of Jerry Cook, a twenty-two-year-old sawmill operator from Byrdstown, Tennessee, makes a wry commentary on the early fears about the use of curare and demonstrates how modern anesthesiologists have learned to control it. In December 1966 Cook cut his hand while out hunting and developed tetanus. He was admitted to St. Mary's Hospital in Knoxville nine days later close to death, in almost continuous convulsions and with a temperature of more than 105 degrees. An anesthesiologist gave him an injection of curare to control the convulsions, performed a tracheotomy and inserted an endotracheal tube—and for no less than three weeks, while a mechanical respirator deputized for his own lungs, Cook was kept completely paralyzed by injections of curare every twenty minutes. Barbiturate injections kept him unconscious and spared him the "living death" described by Claude Bernard and, like Squire Waterton's donkey, he eventually recovered without ill effects.

chapter

14

No surgical operation in the whole of history ever received wider publicity than the one performed in Capetown, South Africa, on December 3, 1967, when Dr. Christiaan Neethling Barnard stitched the heart of a twenty-five-year-old woman into the chest of a middle-aged businessman, Louis Washkansky. Perhaps because many of us still have some lingering atavistic misgivings about William Harvey's three-centuries-old conclusion that the heart is only a highly efficient pump, and not the seat of human love and courage and honor, this spectacular surgical achievement burst upon the public with startling suddenness; it seemed to some to be an achievement utterly without precedent —a step, incredible as it might seem, toward human immortality.

But before the first human heart transplant became a reality, hundreds of blocks had to be laboriously laid in the Great Wall of medical knowledge. One was mortared into place as long ago as 1905, when Dr. Alexis Carrel, a French-born surgeon who spent most of his working life at the Rockefeller Institute, grafted the heart of a small dog into the neck of a larger one; the transplanted heart went on beating for an hour, demonstrating that a

213

heart separated from its parent body could continue to live and function if it received an adequate supply of blood. Years later, in 1936, Carrel devised one of the first primitive artificial hearts, using a pump designed by an unexpected collaborator—Charles A. Lindbergh, the first man to fly the Atlantic alone.

Gradually, through the years, other builders developed foolproof heart-lung machines which supply the patient's body with properly oxygenated blood while the surgeons cut out and replace his heart; yet others contributed to the discovery and understanding (still far from complete) of the phenomenon known as "rejection," the immunological reaction by which the body's natural defenses resist the invasion of alien organs or tissues, and to the development of serums to suppress this reaction and prevent the recipient's body from unwittingly destroying the new heart.

All these contributions and more gave birth to the exciting and rapidly expanding fields of open-heart surgery and kidney transplants, and without the "apprenticeship" they were now able to serve in those fields surgeons could never have dared to attempt a human heart transplant. Neither would this most dramatic of all operations have been possible without the interlocking advances curare brought to anesthesia. For no surgeon would contemplate performing such a radical operation on anyone other than a patient doomed to almost immediate death by his failing heart. And those patients are so weakened by their disease that they are the very worst of "poor risks." All their other organs are likely to have deteriorated, starved of blood by their dying heart's inability to keep it circulating in sufficient quantities. Some last-ditch heart patients, pale and pathetically thin, are so short of breath that they can sleep only propped up with pillows— lying down, they would suffocate—and can speak only in whispers. Many of them have already "died" several times, but have been fortunate enough to suffer their heart failures in a hospital, within reach of prompt resuscitation.

In short, they are classic examples of the type of patient once denied the benefits of surgery—the patient whose weakened system could not have withstood the strain of general anesthesia until curare came along and abolished the general intoxication that had always been the inevitable penalty of a major operation.

More than a quarter of a million North Americans die from

some form of heart disease every year—a sad statistic but one that is not altogether surprising when you consider the extraordinary demands made on the ingeniously fashioned lump of muscle that is the human heart. Weighing less than an ounce at birth (by which time it has already been working for four months) and less than a pound in adulthood (when it is about the size of a fist), the human heart beats about seventy times a minute, or two and a half billion times during an average life span. Working hard, during severe exertion, it can pump a gallon of blood in seven seconds; relaxed, it still puts out more than a gallon a minute—perhaps fifty million gallons in a lifetime.

Actually, the heart is not one pump but two—one to pump blood through the lungs and the other to circulate it around the body. And it does not so much "pump" the blood as squeeze it out with a twisting motion, as a housewife squeezes out a dish cloth with rotating movements of her hands. It consists of four separate chambers—two auricles, or atria, and two ventricles. The atria are reservoirs to hold the blood between strokes of the ventricles, which are the pumps. Blood returning from its circuit of the body is dark-colored and laden with the carbon dioxide it has absorbed in exchange for its oxygen. It is conducted into the right atrium of the heart through two large veins called the superior and inferior vena cava and it waits there for the right ventricle to complete its last pumping stroke. Once this is done, the right ventricle relaxes, a valve opens in the septum, or wall dividing the two chambers, and the dark-colored blood flows through into the ventricle. The valve then closes to prevent the blood returning to the atrium as the ventricle squeezes it through another valve into the pulmonary artery. This large artery divides into two branches, one leading to each lung, and then into smaller vessels culminating in the tiny capillaries in the alveoli of the lung. The dark-colored blood surges through these vessels and on its journey through the lungs gives up its carbon dioxide and absorbs oxygen. Now a bright red, it returns to the left atrium and from there, through another valve, it passes into the largest of the heart's four chambers, the left ventricle. When the left ventricle contracts in its powerful pumping stroke the valve between it and the left atrium closes and another one opens to permit the oxygenated blood to enter the largest blood vessel, the inch-thick aorta, on the first stage of its journey around the body.

Thus, propelled along by the sturdy muscles of the ventricles, the direction it must take governed by the valves, the blood, as Harvey discovered, flows "constantly in a circle" around the body. But occasionally, as it will in any other mechanism, something goes wrong. The heart begins life as a simple tube and the septa, or partitions that divide it into its four chambers, develop during the embryo's first few months in the womb. Sometimes they do not grow completely and the resultant hole in a septum can permit the blood to cross from the right to the left side of the heart without passing through the lungs to be oxygenated, which impairs the supply of oxygen to all the organs and tissues that need it to function efficiently. Or the valves may be damaged by infection, with similar repercussions. Rheumatic fever, for instance, is a common cause of heart disease that usually strikes in childhood and is found more often in girls than in boys. As a result of the bacterial infection associated with it, the delicate flaps of the mitral valve, between the left atrium and left ventricle, become coated with fibrous scar tissue and the opening through which the blood should flow freely becomes constricted.

Poking a finger through one of these blocked valves is often enough to clear it and restore it to its proper function. Small holes in a septum can be stitched closed and larger ones patched. But cutting into a beating heart full of blood is no easy matter and for many years these operations were impossible because of the danger of interrupting the blood supply to the brain and other organs. Later, however, doctors learned to perform them with a technique known as hypothermia—which amounts to refrigeration of the patient. Any chemical reaction, including those constantly going on in the human body, slows down as the temperature drops. And when the body's chemical reactions are slowed down, the brain and other organs need correspondingly less oxygen. So doctors chilled the patient (after anesthetizing him, of course) by rerouting some of his blood through a cooling coil or covering him with crushed ice or a refrigerating blanket. Reducing the body's normal temperature of 98.4 degrees Fahrenheit to 82 degrees enabled the surgeon to work inside the heart for ten minutes instead of the minute or so which is all he can risk without damaging the brain at normal temperatures. Under deep hypothermia, a patient's temperature can be reduced all the way down to 68 degrees, which gives the surgeon more than half an hour to work. But this is a hazardous proceeding and during the past few years it has largely been superseded by use of the heart-lung machine, which not only ensures the body an adequate supply of oxygen but by suspending the action of the heart and lungs entirely gives the surgeon a conveniently motionless area in which to work at his leisure.

Open-heart surgery, as it is called, has saved thousands of lives in recent years and restored many "heart cripples" to health. But it is unable to help the largest class of heart-disease sufferers, those people with disease of the coronary arteries. Twenty-five million North Americans—one person in every nine—have some degree of coronary artery disease; it accounts for 160,000 of the 250,000 heart deaths every year.

As well as pumping the blood to the lungs and around the body, the heart, like any other muscle, must itself be nourished by blood. This task is performed by the coronary arteries, which branch off the aorta close to the heart and run all through the heart's muscle tissues. In a disease called arteriosclerosis, deposits of fibrous tissue build up inside the arteries, hardening them and eventually blocking them. When a blockage occurs within the coronary arteries it cuts off the blood supply to part or all of the heart muscle. This is called a myocardial infarction in medicine —a heart attack by the rest of us. The part of the heart that is starved of blood dies and even if the patient survives the heart attack it is never again able to pull its weight when the rest of the heart muscles contract in unison to pump out the blood. A man's first heart attack is often his last, but some patients survive repeated attacks, having been lucky enough to get prompt medical assistance each time. It is these patients, with a large part of their heart muscle turned into dead and useless scar tissue, who are considered as potential recipients of new hearts—together with victims of myopathies, which are wasting diseases of unknown origin in which the heart muscles become flabby and inefficient.

Because of the moral issues involved, the scarcity of suitable donors, the great financial cost of the operation, and the practical difficulties of giving large numbers of patients adequate care afterwards, heart transplants must still be considered experimental medicine, rather than routine surgery available to all who can benefit from it. But that the operation can be successfully performed at all is a measure of medicine's expanding control over the natural functions of the human body. And because a heart transplant demands the close teamwork of a great number of skilled medical specialists, it is an admirable illustration of the way in which curare has enlarged the anesthesiologist's capacity and responsibilities far beyond anything that could have been imagined by the old "rag-and-bottle" artists.

There are, of course, two medical teams engaged in any heart transplant—one to remove the donor's heart and the other to place it unharmed in the recipient's chest. As many as twenty or more highly trained people may be involved on both teams— surgeons, anesthesiologists, heart and brain specialists, immunologists, bacteriologists, hematologists, nurses, and technicians. Many more are needed to support them in the laboratory, where the blood and tissues of prospective donor and recipient are put through a battery of tests to ensure that they match as closely as possible, and where such critical factors as the acid-base balance of their blood are constantly checked.

A hospital equipped to perform heart transplants—it needs twin operating rooms side by side and sterile rooms to house the recipient for the first few weeks after the operation—seldom has any lack of potential recipients. Finding a donor is more difficult: he or she must be in otherwise good health but suffering from irreversible brain damage caused by an accident or a stroke— the rupture of a blood vessel in the brain. Often the potential donor is found in a hospital other than the one where the transplant is to be performed; in this case, several doctors go along to assess his suitability. A neurologist and a neurosurgeon satisfy themselves that he can never recover—that there is not even an outside chance of his brain damage being repaired, or repairing itself; that the brain—and thus the patient—is in fact already dead, and that the heart is being kept alive only by artificial respiration. A cardiologist examines him and checks his medical history and electrocardiogram—a tracing of the pattern made by the heart's electrical impulses—to make sure the heart is healthy and has not been damaged in the accident or by the patient's illness.

Then it is the turn of the immunologist, who may be a physician or a biologist or both, and who specializes in the study of the various factors involved in immunity to disease. For the phenomenon of "rejection," the biggest barrier to the success of any organ transplant, is a result of the body's otherwise desirable ability to manufacture effective defenses against alien substances —whether they be disease-causing bacteria or the heart, kidney, or even skin of a person with a different genetic makeup; its ability, in other words, to "immunize" itself against foreign invasion. The immunologist's task, which is performed in the laboratory, is to establish which of the potential recipients awaiting a new heart most closely matches the blood and tissues of the donor; which of their bodies is likely to react least against the invasion of the alien heart.

Since no two persons have identical genes, a perfect match is unattainable. But there is a scale to measure degrees of compatibility. The closest match possible in theory, designated as "A" on this scale, is between a potential recipient and his identical twin—though the odds against one twin's healthy heart becoming available just when it is needed by the other are obviously astronomical. The next closest match (A^1) is between the recipient and his brother or sister; the next (A^2) between the recipient and his parents or close relatives; and the next (A^3) between the recipient and distant relatives. The designation "B" on the scale is given to a reasonably close match for nonrelated persons, and "C" is defined as "acceptable."

The matching procedure is critical, since if the blood and tissues of donor and recipient are completely incompatible rejection follows swiftly and disastrously. In a really bad match, the new heart would immediately become the battleground on which the body's natural defenders made their stand; as the battle raged, it would become swollen and discolored and within as little as fifteen minutes it could be completely destroyed.

Understanding of this immunological reaction dates only from 1944. For many years before that it had been known that while skin grafted from one part of a person's body to another would grow quite satisfactorily in its new location, skin grafted from one person to another would not "take"; no matter how doctors tried, the alien tissue was always rejected. No one knew why, but the problem eventually engaged the attention of the distinguished British scientist Sir Peter Medawar, whose achievements in medicine were recognized in 1960 by the award of the Nobel Prize. Medawar had been carrying out a clinical study of patients burned during World War II and in 1944 he performed a series of experiments on rabbits. He grafted a patch of skin from one rabbit to another and waited for it to die and slough off. Then he performed another graft on the same site. The second and any subsequent grafts always died faster than the first one had, and Medawar concluded that the body of the host rabbit had manufactured some substance to reject them.

Doctors knew no way of counteracting this immunological reaction when kidney transplants were first attempted, in the early 1950s. (Kidneys, which get rid of the body's waste products, were the first organs doctors tried to replace by transplantation because while their complete breakdown eventually results in death, the body can get along without them for several days, which gives the surgeon more than enough time to remove and replace them; in contrast, the body can survive without the heart or lungs for only a few minutes, unless their function is continued artificially, which has only become possible in recent years.) Fifteen kidney transplants were performed between 1951 and 1953. Without any treatment to suppress the immunological reaction, most of the kidneys were rejected within a few weeks, though one survived for five months, presumably because the donor and the recipient were a good match. In 1958, X-rays began to be used to irradiate the patient's whole body in an attempt to neutralize the bodily organisms responsible for the immunological reaction. Unfortunately, the first patient subjected to this treatment died from radiation sickness thirty-two days later, and it was small consolation to his doctors to discover that otherwise the treatment had succeeded: the kidney showed no evidence of rejection. The dangers of X-ray therapy are such that today it is only kept in reserve as a second line of defense if the rejection cannot be controlled with drugs.

The breakthrough doctors needed came in England in 1959, when it was discovered that the immunological reaction could be controlled after a transplant by giving the patient injections of a drug called 6-mercaptopurine, though at the cost of some undesirable repercussions on the patient's blood. Later a less toxic drug called azathioprine was developed and this is still used today, though it too has unwanted side-effects. The mechanism of the immunological reaction is still only imperfectly understood, but it is known that transplanted organs are attacked by white blood cells called lymphocytes. The trouble with azathioprine is that while it suppresses the lymphocytes it also knocks out other white blood cells called leukocytes, which defend the body against bacterial infections. This is why patients with new hearts must be isolated in sterile rooms after the operation. A further advance was the introduction of "antilymphocytic" serum, which suppresses the lymphocytes selectively, without harming the leukocytes. This is obtained by injecting extracts from the human thymus gland, which manufactures lymphocytes, into horses and other animals; the serum is produced by the animals' own immunological reaction to the human lymphocytes.

Observing the reaction of the white blood cells when blood samples of the donor and the prospective recipients are mixed is one of the tests the immunologist makes in advance to determine how severe the rejection reaction is likely to be; he watches under a microscope and if twenty percent or more of the white cells are knocked out by the reaction, donor and recipient are incompatible. It might be thought that compatible donors and recipients would always belong to the same blood group, but this is not invariably the case; there are so many other factors involved, such as the cross-matching of tissues, that sometimes a recipient belonging to a blood group other than the donor's is found to be a better match than one from the same group. There are dozens of such tests, far too complicated to be described in detail here, and completing them takes from four to eight hours. During this time, the donor is cared for by one of the anesthesiologists on the transplant team.

Assuming that the donor's heart has been found to be healthy, the anesthesiologist must ensure that it remains so. Since the unconscious donor is being kept "alive" only by the mechanical respirator, he is in the same dependent situation as a patient during an operation, and the anesthesiologist must keep a close watch on his blood pressure, acid-base balance, and all the other factors which must be controlled to prevent the condition of his heart from deteriorating before the transplant. Though this is one patient the anesthesiologist cannot bring back from that journey down the road that ends in death, he must exercise the same skill and care as he does with a living patient to save at least the heart. He may give drugs to maintain the circulation of the blood, soda bicarbonate to correct its acid-base balance, and perhaps transfusions to maintain the normal blood volume.

He also gives the donor a strong dose of antibiotics to counteract any latent infection that may be communicated to the recipient. Since the donor is to all intents and purposes dead, it is quite possible for his heart to fail. This actually happened during one of the first heart transplants performed in the Institut de Cardiologie in Montreal. The donor's heart stopped beating just as the surgeons in the next room were beginning to open the recipient's chest. Fortunately the doctors were able to connect the heart to the heart-lung machine and keep it alive until the recipient was ready for it, and the operation was completed successfully.

When the time comes for the donor to be moved to the hospital where the transplant is to be performed, he must be taken off the mechanical respirator. At this point his death will become complete unless his breathing is supported in some other way. And so the anesthesiologist connects a portable respirator to the endotracheal tube or the tracheotomy opening in his throat and walks alongside the patient, his hand rhythmically squeezing the rebreathing bag that operates the portable respirator, as the stretcher is wheeled to the ambulance. The donor's survival is thus quite literally in the anesthesiologist's hands throughout the ambulance journey and until he is linked up to the mechanical respirator in the operating room where his heart will be removed. The anesthesiologist is a busy man on that ambulance ride. In addition to breathing for the donor he must also regularly check his blood pressure and heartbeat and even in emergencies give a blood transfusion or injections to stimulate the heart.

A potential recipient's physical preparation for a heart transplant begins as much as eight hours before the operation, perhaps before the donor has even arrived at the hospital, but his mental preparation, which is just as important, has begun days or weeks earlier. He must first decide for himself that he wants the operation, and then a committee of doctors which includes cardiologists, surgeons, and anesthesiologists must decide on his suitability for it. His motivation is carefully weighed—sometimes it amounts to no more than a disguised suicidal tendency—and he must satisfy the doctors that he really wants to take this chance of extending his life span, if only for a limited period; he must be prepared to cooperate, to fight the battle against rejection and infection—incarceration in the sterile room for weeks after the operation can have disastrous effects on his morale; and after his discharge from the hospital he might have to change his whole way of life, turning up at the hospital every second day or twice a week for painful injections of drugs to suppress his immunological reaction. If the doctors decide the man is intelligent, understands the risks of the transplant and the demands it will make on him, and is prepared to cooperate, they must still assess his physical suitability for the operation. Arteriosclerosis is a generalized disease which will have affected all his other organs to some extent, and so the doctors look for a patient who, despite the desperate condition of his heart, retains enough general health to both withstand and benefit from the transplant; it is no good giving a new heart to a man who is likely to die the next week from a brain hemorrhage or a breakdown of his kidneys.

Once a recipient has convinced the doctors that he is physically and mentally able to stand the strain of the operation, he begins the nerve-racking wait for a donor to be found. The anesthesiologist visits him regularly to acquaint himself with his medical history, his general condition, and his mental state, which governs the amount of sedation he will need to assist him in his ordeal. Soon after a potential donor is found, the immunologist's first series of tests narrows down the number of possible recipients for his heart to perhaps two patients. While the immunologist conducts more detailed tests to arrive at the final choice, both these patients will be prepared for the operation. They receive injections of antilymphocytic serum and immunosuppressive drugs to forestall the body's immunological mechanism and prevent it from rejecting the new heart as soon as it is sewn into place. And they are dosed with antibiotics to anticipate the danger of infection.

Eventually, one man is chosen as the closest match to the donor; the man who will now be permitted to gamble his last few days or weeks of life for a reprieve that may be only too short-lived. About an hour before the operation is due to begin, he is given an injection of a tranquilizing drug to ease his anxiety—a nervous patient's heart is likely to be fluttering wildly and may collapse with the first shock of the anesthetic. The injection leaves him mildly befuddled but calm and still able to understand and cooperate with the doctors and nurses as he is wheeled into the operating room.

If he is still sufficiently aware of his surroundings to care, he will find the operating room crowded with a bewildering array of machinery, both mechanical and electrical; a maze of tubes and wiring linking cylinders and pumps and measuring devices, grouped in a kind of orderly chaos which would gladden the eye of a set designer engaged on a science-fiction movie. At the head of the operating table, on a trolley, stands the anesthetic machine, its cylinders and taps connected by flexible corrugated tubing to the rubber mask which will later be replaced by the endotracheal tube. Hooked into this is the mechanical respirator, and a machine stands nearby with gauges whose oscillating needles will soon display every fluctuation of the patient's blood pressure to the anesthesiologist's watchful eyes. Off to one side, ready to be moved into position when it is needed, is the machine that makes the operation possible: the heart-lung machine. And somewhere, probably on the wall at the foot of the table, where the anesthesiologist can constantly keep it in view, there will be a cardioscope, a screen like a television screen on which an electrical pulse will trace the beating of the patient's diseased heart until the surgeons still it forever.

The anesthesiologist greets the patient as he is wheeled into the operating room and helps the nurses and orderlies lift him on a sheet and position him properly on the table. Now comes the loneliest moment of the patient's life. Within a few minutes he will be put to sleep and soon the mysterious processes by which he lives, those processes which alone distinguish him from the dead, will be going on somewhere among these still-silent machines. When he wakes, it will be with a dead man's heart beating in his chest. No man ever embarked on a more frightening journey. And yet, such are the reserves of human fortitude, many of those who have faced this ordeal have done so with no more than the average preoperative dose of tranquilizing drug.

Now the man who will conduct the patient on his venturing beyond the brink of death speaks a few reassuring words as he takes up his arm and injects a local anesthetic into his wrist. When this has taken effect, he implants a measuring needle through the numb spot into the radial artery; connected to one of the machines, this gives an accurate and continuous reading of the blood pressure in the patient's arteries during the critical period when anesthesia is being induced and throughout the operation. Next, the anesthesiologist finds a vein higher up the patient's arm and gives him the injection of thiopentone which glides him into unconsciousness within seconds. The patient feels nothing now as the anesthesiologist inserts a cannula, or small tube, into the vein to serve as an open channel for any substance that must be injected into the bloodstream during or immediately after the operation.

The first of the many drugs that will enter the body through this cannula during the next six hours is curare—usually the quick-acting synthetic form, succinylcholine. The patient's neck muscles strain momentarily, his fingers twitch feebly at his sides, his chest heaves—and quite suddenly he is still. The curare has relaxed his whole body and overcome the resistance of the chest and diaphragm so that the anesthesiologist can now take over and control his breathing. He places his rubber mask over the patient's nose and mouth. But before he begins to administer the anesthetic he squeezes the rebreathing bag to pump pure oxygen into the lungs for a minute or so; the patient's system is already likely to be partly starved of oxygen by the inefficiency of his debilitated heart, and this gives him a reserve supply to carry him through his intubation. Satisfied that his patient is well oxygenated, the anesthesiologist removes the mask, tilts his head back, and slips the endotracheal tube down between the now-limp muscles of his throat and windpipe. The tube connects his lungs to the mechanical respirator, preset to deliver the amount of ventilation required, and the anesthesiologist now begins to feed in the anesthetic—usually the innocuous nitrous oxide.

When the induction of anesthesia is complete, the nurses remove the green sheet that has covered the patient since he entered the operating room and he lies naked, looking pathetically frail and defenseless as the work of preparing him for the surgeons goes on. The most stringent precautions are taken against infection, and a nurse swabs and mops his whole body repeatedly with an antiseptic solution. Those parts of his body that will not be touched by the surgeons are then wrapped with sterile towels and over his chest is draped a sheet of plastic which adheres to his skin and seals off his pores from any bacteria that might lodge there; the surgeons cut through the plastic and it remains

225

in place until after he is stitched up. A catheter is inserted into his bladder and taped to his leg—all the fluids lost by his body during the next few hours will be carefully measured and analyzed and the results reported to the anesthesiologist, who decides how and when they should be replaced; even the swabs and sponges used to soak up the blood he loses during the operation are carefully collected and weighed so that the anesthesiologist can maintain his correct blood volume. Electrodes are taped to his skin near his shoulders to monitor his heartbeat on the cardioscope, and a tiny electrical thermometer is pushed down his esophagus, or gullet, close to his heart, to register its temperature while the blood is being circulated through the heart-lung machine.

While all this is being done, the anesthesiologist implants another measuring needle into the jugular vein in the patient's neck, to monitor the blood pressure in his veins, which is important when the blood is being directed through the heart-lung machine. And before the surgeons begin their incisions, many anesthesiologists prefer to switch from the more potent succinylcholine used for the intubation to injections of the pure *d*-tubocurarine, one injection of which will keep the patient relaxed for as much as half an hour with no ill effects. Because light anesthesia is so vital in heart transplants, the anesthetic mixture may be as little as fifty percent nitrous oxide with fifty percent oxygen. This is not a heavy enough concentration of nitrous oxide to keep a patient properly "under" and so it is supplemented with an injection of an analgesic, or pain-relieving, narcotic drug such as meperidine.

The anesthetized patient, his muscles completely relaxed by curare and his breathing being carried on for him by the mechanical respirator, is now handed over to the surgeons. Their first cut is a long vertical incision down the center of his chest. As the flesh is drawn back the severed blood vessels are sealed by an electric cautery to prevent bleeding, and eventually the incision reveals the patient's sternum, or breastbone. An electric saw divides this down the center—it will be wired together again after the operation—and the ribs are drawn back and held by steel instruments called retractors. The surgeon then reaches into this gaping hole in the chest and cuts into the pericardium, the sheath of tissue in which the heart and great blood vessels are encased, to expose the still-beating heart.

As the two or three surgeons gathered around the chest begin their work, another surgeon makes an incision in the patient's thigh to expose and isolate his femoral artery and femoral vein, which are connected to the heart-lung machine. Another connection is made inside the chest, to the superior vena cava, the great vein that brings blood from the upper part of the body back to the heart. Perhaps an hour after the first incision, the surgeons are ready for the blood to be rerouted away from the heart, and the heart-lung machine is started.

Essentially, the task performed by the machine, developed since World War II, is simple: it merely oxygenates and pumps the blood. That it took so long to design a man-made device to perform these functions is an indication of the ingenuity and efficiency of the equipment nature designed for the job. First of all, no ordinary mechanical pump is suitable: rapidly moving surfaces would damage or destroy the delicate blood cells. And so the blood is squeezed along through plastic tubes by moving rollers or artificial fingers. Secondly, the insides of these tubes must be absolutely sterile and as smooth as man can make them; rough surfaces would not only damage the blood but would tend to cause it to clot, and clots in the blood vessels can be fatal. Man has not yet begun to approach nature in this—the endothelium, or lining of our blood vessels, is smoother than any substance it has so far been found possible to produce artificially, which is one reason why heart-lung machines cannot be used to circulate the blood for more than a few hours at most. Thirdly, since the tubes of the machine and the patient's blood vessels must form a closed circuit from which the smallest air bubble is rigorously excluded, the pump must be primed in advance; the whole of its interior must be filled either with blood— which may present some difficulty if the patient has a rare blood type—or with a saline solution containing five percent dextrose, a form of sugar found in blood. While it dilutes the patient's blood, this does no harm and is easily eliminated from his body by his kidneys after the operation.

In the lungs, as we have seen, the oxygen-for-carbon dioxide exchange takes place through the fine walls of the alveoli, without the blood and the air coming into contact. Man cannot reproduce

227

this system, so he must find some other way of getting the oxygen into the blood. There are various methods of achieving this. In some machines, oxygen is circulated around several mesh screens, like window screens; the blood is dribbled down over the screens and, thus spread out over a large surface, it picks up oxygen as it goes. Another system is to blow a stream of oxygen across a series of revolving stainless steel discs; the discs dip into a trough through which the blood flows and on each rotation pick up a film of blood and expose it to the oxygen. But the method most commonly used in North America is to bubble oxygen slowly upward through a column of blood. Machines using this system must be equipped with some device to remove the bubbles before they enter the patient's bloodstream.

The heart-lung machine is operated by technicians under the supervision of the anesthesiologist. The carbon-dioxide-laden blood which would otherwise return to the heart is diverted into the machine from the superior (or upper) vena cava and from the femoral vein, which drains the inferior (or lower) vena cava; and it is pumped back into the body through the femoral artery—in fact while the machine is in operation the blood is circulated in the opposite direction to its normal flow, traveling around the body from the thigh instead of the heart. But this has no ill effects on the patient.

Once the blood is being oxygenated and circulated by the machine, there is no further need for the lungs, so the anesthesiologist ceases to inflate them with the mechanical respirator. This is a convenience to the surgeons—it gives them a still chest in which to work as they clamp off the great blood vessels before severing the aorta and the pulmonary artery and cutting out the heart. But it also deprives the anesthesiologist of the route by which he administers the nitrous oxide, so to keep the patient under during the two hours or so that his blood is being artificially circulated he continues the anesthesia by feeding narcotics, barbiturates, or halothane directly into the blood as it courses through the machine.

Suddenly the fluorescent dot that has been dancing across the cardioscope with every beat of the patient's heart disappears: the scalpel has done its task and the useless heart is now lifted out of the body. Its diseased areas, dead tissue that has long since ceased to perform any useful function, are clearly visible. Yet such is the tenacity of the surviving muscle tissue that if you flick the excised heart with your finger it will twitch like a dying fish, and this "irritability" can persist for as long as an hour after the heart has been taken out of the body.

While the recipient's heart is being removed, the donor's heart is also being cut out in a parallel operation in the next room. Now it is brought in, pink and healthy, resting on a sterile towel. The surgeon has left parts of both atria of the recipient's heart in place, attached to their blood vessels—this way he has to rejoin only two blood vessels, the aorta and the pulmonary artery, instead of eight. He places the donor's heart in the cavity in the chest and begins to stitch the atria of old and new hearts together, rolling the new heart into position as he works. Then he sews up the aorta and pulmonary artery, squeezes the heart with his hands to empty it of air, removes the clamps on the blood vessels to permit the blood to resume its normal course—and that little dot begins to dance across the cardioscope screen again. Sometimes the new heart needs an electric shock to jolt it into resuming its concerted rhythm, but often it starts on its own.

The anesthesiologist restarts the mechanical respirator, the patient's lungs resume their activity, and the heart-lung machine is drained into his blood vessels and switched off. It is now three or four hours since the operation began, and all this time the anesthesiologist has been standing watch over the patient, with the help of his various monitoring devices and the periodic reports handed to him from the laboratory which, throughout the operation, carries out analyses of the patient's blood and any fluids lost by his body. From time to time, as well as maintaining the anesthesia, he gives the patient an injection: curare, if the muscular relaxation begins to wear off, soda bicarbonate if the acid-base balance of the blood requires it, and various body fluids if and when they are needed. As the surgeons complete their task, closing the pericardium, wiring the breastbone, and finally stitching up the wound, the anesthesiologist gives the patient a blood transfusion, not so much to make up the blood lost during the operation—strangely, not much blood *is* lost—but to renew its power to clot, which is deliberately suspended with an anticoagulating drug at the start of the operation.

From five to six hours after he entered the operating room, the patient is lifted back onto the stretcher and wheeled into the sterile room where he will spend the next few weeks. Within minutes of being eased into his bed, he awakes from the anesthetic, his new heart pulsing bravely in his chest. Incredibly, as little as six hours after the operation he may make his first tentative steps around his room, helped by his doctors or nurses. He is sore, of course, but sedative drugs dull the pain of the dramatic assault that has been made on his body. He has no racking headache, no fits of nausea, no attacks of painful retching. His system has not been soaked and poisoned by the anesthetic and he will not lie for days in a fog of suffering as his body seeks to shake off the debilitating effects of "general intoxication." This is the revolution in anesthesia brought about by curare's long journey from the jungle to civilization.

It is not yet a century since the British surgeon Sir John Erichsen pronounced that "the abdomen, the chest, and the brain will be forever shut from the intrusion of the wise and humane surgeon." The wise and humane surgeon can now, like his miraculous Chinese predecessor Pien Ch'iao twenty-three centuries ago, "interchange" men's hearts. It is an extraordinary achievement—and it would not have been possible without old Friar Martyr's "venomous arrowes."

epilogue

The story of curare would not be complete without a final look
at the later careers of two of the men whose vision and faith
and courage combined to bring about the revolution in anesthesia.

Richard Gill, who hobbled into the jungle leaning on his stick
and emerged six months later with the pots of raw poison that
made it all possible, led a life that was part triumph, part tragedy.
His failure to land the contract to supply Squibb with curare
was the most crushing of many disappointments he suffered during his ill-starred career. It not only shattered his plans to return
to Ecuador with a flourishing business; it relegated him to little
more than a spectator's role in the drama that was about to
unfold. But the man was indefatigable. Just as he never accepted
his doctor's verdict that he had multiple sclerosis, he refused to
accept the medical evidence that curare could not cure spastic
paralysis. If, as the doctors said, the drug's action was too transient
to benefit spastic patients, then some slow-acting form of it must
be evolved which, being released into the bloodstream gradually,
would loosen locked muscles for long periods without causing a

general paralysis; some preparation which could be taken regularly, like insulin, and which would permit spastic cripples to walk again. And if doctors could not discover or develop such a preparation then he, Richard Gill, would do it.

In 1943 Gill moved to California. He wanted to be near a university to pursue his researches and he chose Stanford. He settled in Palo Alto and established a laboratory in the garage of his house on El Camino Real, the King's Highway. Jokingly, he used to call it "the only arrow-poison factory in the world." Not surprisingly, his neighbors failed to appreciate the joke. His unusual laboratory and the sinister smells emanating from it distressed them considerably. But such trifles as complaints from neighbors could not divert Gill from his grand design.

He gave himself a cram course in chemistry and pharmacology by his usual method of talking to the people who knew about these things, and eventually developed his own process for extracting the alkaloid from supplies of curare he had flown to him regularly from Ecuador. After the war, when its use spread to hospitals in Europe, he sold purified curare by the kilo in Germany, France, and Austria, as well as in the United States. He lectured to medical associations and kept up his missionary work for the "flying death" in articles and books.

And all the time he was trying to develop his slow-acting form of the drug. He tried various expedients designed to release it into the bloodstream gradually, such as dissolving it in peanut oil, without success. Then he produced it in tablets intended to be held under the tongue for half an hour until they dissolved. In 1953 he wrote to A. E. Bennett, his first ally, expressing his confidence that this would "complete the final taming of curare" and adding: "We should make a very tangible and literal 'million or so.'"

Alas for his hopes, he could convince no drug company that his tablets had the slightest value; they aroused no more interest than had his ideas for an oral contraceptive and an infallible hair restorer years before. But Dr. William B. Neff, former chairman of the department of anesthesia at Stanford, who collaborated with Gill in his early days in California, still has some of the tablets. He has occasionally given them to friends suffering from muscular stiffness after the unaccustomed exertion of a day on the tennis courts or the ski slopes. And, he says, they remove

232

the pain of stiff muscles for about four or five hours without any apparent ill-effect on other parts of the body.

"In view of the difficulty of getting scientific evidence that there is a level of *d*-tubocurarine built up in the bloodstream I have been reluctant to say anything about it," Neff told me during the writing of this book. "Perhaps it's witchcraft," he added with a smile, "but if so it's an interesting way of demonstrating the efficacy of these jungle remedies."

The search for a slow-acting form of curare was not just the obsession of a chronic misfit. It has been carried on by medical researchers on both sides of the Atlantic and though it has never succeeded some doctors continue to hope that one day an alkaloid with this property may be found in the laboratory or in one of the many curare vines whose properties still await thorough investigation.

In his later years, Gill was afflicted by a series of illnesses, some of them perhaps traceable to the multiple sclerosis he refused to acknowledge. He developed osteoarthritis in his hip and could get around only on crutches or in a wheelchair. Also, his financial worries and repeated disappointments took a sad psychological toll; he became unnaturally suspicious and was convinced that people were persecuting him. He died on July 7, 1958, from the massive hemorrhage of an ulcer.

It was a bitter ending to a career that with better luck might have brought Richard Gill fame, if not fortune. He never made the million he wanted so badly, and he died a disillusioned and disappointed man. But it was his enterprise, his persistence, his persuasiveness—and his near-mystical faith in the twenty-five pounds of *brujo's* black magic he brought back from Ecuador—that spurred other better-qualified men to bridge the gap separating jungle from civilization and put the "flying death" to work in the operating room.

Time was kinder to the key figure in the curare story. Though Harold Griffith's whole career until 1942 had been spent as a working doctor in a little-known hospital with no teaching department, he had trained a steady flow of postgraduate students whose teachers had advised them to go to Montreal if they wanted to sit at the feet of a master. In 1946 his achievements were finally recognized by his alma mater, McGill University, and he was appointed lecturer in anesthesia—at the age of fifty-two.

233

Four years later, he became a full professor and chairman of the department.

But he continued to run his own hospital—he had taken over as unpaid medical superintendent when his father died in 1936—and to practice anesthesia, until the age of seventy-two. And right up to his retirement he was at work in the operating room before eight in the morning, envied by his much younger colleagues for his quick grasp of the essentials of any new technique or development—anything that "filled a need" in the profession to which he contributed so much.

In 1951 Griffith was elected chairman of an international committee set up to organize a world-wide organization of anesthesiologists with the aim of promoting better standards of anesthesia in all countries—at that time, about half of all the properly qualified anesthesiologists in the world were in the United States and the overwhelming majority of the rest were in Britain, Canada, and other English-speaking countries, where the practice of anesthesia has always been considered a medical specialty. The World Federation of Societies of Anesthesiologists was formed in 1955, with Griffith as its president, and the original membership of twenty-six countries had increased to sixty by 1968. When Griffith retired from active direction of the Federation in 1960, he was appointed founder president for life.

Though his name remained unknown to the general public, his contributions to anesthesia were recognized through the years by many international honors within his profession, including the Distinguished Service Award of the American Society of Anesthesiologists and the Henry Hill Hickman Medal awarded by the Royal Society of Medicine in Britain in memory of the country surgeon who dosed puppies with carbon dioxide and cut off their tails without pain, and then tragically failed to convince a heedless world that he had discovered anesthesia.

Perhaps the best summing-up of Harold Griffith's achievement came from Professor T. Cecil Gray, who pioneered the technique of light anesthesia and controlled respiration in Britain. In 1967, in his capacity as dean of the faculty of anesthesia of the Royal College of Surgeons, Gray wrote to Griffith inviting him to be guest of honor at a dinner held by the College in London to commemorate the twenty-fifth anniversary of the introduction of curare into the operating room. "We are all convinced," he wrote, "that this had the same significance to our specialty as Listerian antisepsis had to surgery."

As for curare itself, many tribes have lost their traditional knowledge of how to prepare it as the use of firearms has spread deeper into Amazonia. But curare made in the old way, laced with snake venom and ants' stings, is still an item of trade in remote areas. And the development of synthetic relaxant drugs has by no means ended civilization's need for the raw native poison. Several drug companies on both sides of the Atlantic extract *d*-tubocurarine from it and the Astoria company still supplies it to Squibb. A recent shipment totaled 660 kilos—almost three quarters of a ton of the dark, sticky mess which was still so rare a generation ago that medical researchers were reduced to using museum specimens thirty years old.

While the curare used daily in the great hospitals of North America is still produced in the jungle, its preparation is now supervised by an Astoria field man, a Peruvian of Spanish extraction who is reputed to have been kidnapped by Indians as a boy and to have learned all the *brujos'* secrets. He can recognize the *Chondodendron tomentosum* vine at a glance, and this is the only ingredient he permits to enter the poison. Astoria collects its vines in an area on the Río do Sisa, a small tributary of the Huallaga river, which flows into the Marañón and thence into the Amazon. The procedure has not changed much since it was described by an Astoria botanist, Frederick Vogel, in a report written in 1946. The field man still faces a seven-hundred-mile journey from the company's headquarters at Iquitos, an ocean port on the Amazon more than two thousand miles from the sea. He can fly part of the way, but there are no roads in the area where the vines grow and the last part of his journey must be accomplished by canoe or balsa raft. As Vogel described it, one stage of the journey which takes an hour if you are lucky enough to have an airplane takes a minimum of one and a half days by truck. And if the weather is bad it can take as much as forty-five days. "Plan on plenty of delay," Vogel wrote. "Add at least thirty days to the rough time estimate. Transportation is undependable; labor is unpredictable; rain is probable; and nobody seems to care about time except you."

Despite these difficulties, as medicine's demand for curare has grown, mass production has replaced black magic in its prepara-

235

tion. Jungle Indians still pound the vines and boil down their extract, but they are hired laborers and not witch doctors. The "flying death" still bubbles over jungle fires, but in steel drums instead of clay pots. And it reaches civilization not in calabashes or primitively decorated bamboo tubes, but in five-gallon lard cans.

Index

Artificial respiration, use of curare with, 76, 86, 100, 103, 105, 112, 189, 195, 202, 206-12. *See also* Respiration, controlled
Artists, medical practice and, 19
Asbestosis, 210
Asklepios, 8-9
Assyrians, 24, 46
Aspirin, 114
Astoria Pan-Americana, Inc., 145-46, 235
Atropine, 92
Augustine, Saint, 15
Australian aborigines, 5, 49
Automobile accident victims, controlled respiration for, 210-11
Avellina rosada, 128-29
Avicenna, 25
Azathioprine, 220-21
Aztecs, 53

Bailly, Nicolas, 17
Balboa, Vasco Núñez de, 53, 54
Bancroft, Edward Bartholomew, 66-68
Barbasco, 64
Barbers, practice of surgery by, 16
Barbiturate poisoning, 211
Barnard, Christiaan N, 7, 213
Battlefield casualties and surgery, 6, 8, 12-13, 18, 25, 111; use of curare, 202-5
Bee stings, 50-51
Beecher, Henry K., 201-3
Bellevue Hospital, N.Y.C., 109, 168
Bennett, A. E., 135-47, 148, 149, 166-68, 189, 194, 232
Bernard, Claude, 58, 88, 93-100, 111
Bini, Dr., 140
Birth control, 129-30
Bladder stones, 16-17, 24
Blegdam Hospital, Copenhagen, 205-7
Blood (blood circulation), 205-12: acid-base balance, 208-12; anesthesia and, 161-63, 205-12, 216-29; early study of, 20-22; organ transplants and, 214, 216-22; rejection process and, 218-22
Blood poisoning, 38, 39, 40
Blow darts (blow pipes), 65, 70-71, 83-85, 128
Boehm, Rudolf, 113, 170
Bolívar, Simón, 113
Boussingault, Jean Baptiste, 113
Bows and arrows, poisoned, 45-61 *passim*, 65, 83-85, 87, 89, 108, 118
Boyle, Robert, 22
Brain: anesthesia and surgery on, 41, 154, 159-63; effect of curare on, 95-100; anesthesia, pain and, 154, 159-63
Brazil, 63
Breathing: controlled, 205-12, 213-30 *passim*; effect of curare on, 76, 86, 100, 102, 105, 112, 167-87, 188-212 *passim*, 226 (*see also* Artificial respiration)
British Guiana, 78, 88
British Encyclopedia of Medical Practice, 112-13
British Medical Journal, 65
Brocklesby, Richard, 72-73

Brodie, Benjamin Collins, 76-77, 86, 87, 103, 189
Burman, Michael, 131-34, 138

Caesarean operations, 7, 39
Caffeine, 92
Calendula solution, 173
Canada (Canadians), 171-87, 188-95, 203, 222, 233-35. *See also* specific individuals, places
Carbolic acid, 40
Carbon dioxide, 27-28; and oxygen exchange, 207-12, 227-29
Carbon monoxide, 74, 162
Cardioscope, 224
Caribbean islands, 52ff. *See also* specific islands
Caroni, river, 60, 62
Carotid arteries, 24
Carpue, Joseph, 6-7
Carrel, Alexis, 213-14
Carter, Jay Bailey, 184
Cassini, Jacques, 63
Castillo, Bernal Díaz del, 53
Castration, 8
Cats, rabid, 105
Cels, 46
Cerebral palsy, 125, 133
Cerletti, Dr., 140
Charles I, of Spain, 47
Chazula Indians, 134
Cheselden, William, 24
Chibcha Indians, 60
Childbirth, 7, 12, 17 (*see also* Birth control); tetanus in, 109
Children (*see also* Birth control; Childbirth): capacity for pain in, 153; spastic paralysis in, 177ff, 131ff, 141
Chimborazo, Mount, 64, 69
China, 7-8
Chloroform, use of, 41, 175, 182, 183, 184, 199; addiction to, 35-36
Cholesterol, 114
Cholo Indians, 50
Chondodendron tomentosum, 90-100, 134-35, 145, 148-50, 235-36
Chorea, 15
Christians (Christianity), 15, 16, 54, 58
Churchill, Frederick, 37-38
Circumcision, 5
Cleanliness, surgical, 5, 38ff. *See also* Infection
Clostridium tetani, 107-8
Coca tree, 102, 155-59
Cocaine, 102, 155-59
Codeine, 92
Colt, Samuel, 28, 32
Colton, Gardner Quincy, 28-30
Columbus, Christopher, second expedition of, 52, 53
Conquistadors, 52ff, 155
Controlled respiration. *See* Respiration, controlled
Cook, Jerry, 212
Cooley, use of laughing gas on, 29
Coronary artery disease, 217
Cos, 9

240

241

K42